AN ILLUSTRATED
HISTORY OF
TRACTORS

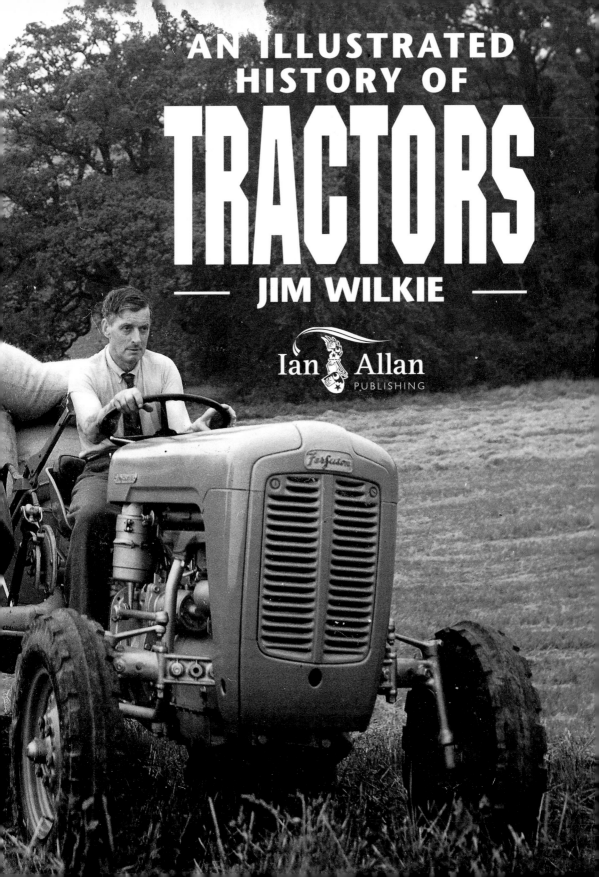

AN ILLUSTRATED
HISTORY OF
TRACTORS

— JIM WILKIE —

Ian Allan
PUBLISHING

Front cover, main image: Modern tractors like the Case International (right) and Massey Ferguson (left) are now usually specified with four-wheel drive. Together they make quick work of harvesting and loading potatoes for storage. *Peter Adams*

Front cover, inset: Yet in the late 1940s the Field Marshall was classed as a powerful tractor. *Author*

Back cover, main image: By the 1960s limited weather protection was offered by the optional Lambourn cab on this Nuffield 4/60. *Alan C. Butcher*

Back cover, inset: John Deere were quick to realise that a spacious cab and light controls were important to get the highest output from drivers. *Alan C. Butcher*

Half title page: Despite disappointing sales the Ferguson Brown launched in 1936 marked the start of a radical change in tractor design. *Ian Allan Library*

Title page: Twenty years later the Ferguson 35 was launched. The rear set axle on the trailer imposed a heavy load on the drawbar. This was taken by the hydraulic pick up hitch which speeded coupling even a loaded trailer. *Ian Allan Library*

CONTENTS

First published 1999

ISBN 0 7110 2625 4

Published by Ian Allan Publishing

an imprint of Ian Allan Publishing Ltd, Terminal House, Shepperton, Surrey TW17 8AS.

Printed by Ian Allan Printing Ltd, Riverdene Business Park, Hersham, Surrey KT12 4RG.

Code: 9904/B

Introduction

In order for you to survive, your body must have food to eat. Only in the last 50 years has it been possible to take a supply of cheap, nutritious food for granted in most parts of the world. For this we have to thank the work of farmers, helped by the agricultural tractor. Plant and animal breeders have done excellent work, as have scientists researching sprays and fertilisers, but it took farmers to make use of their work. Certainly better transport and shipping have got the food to where it is needed with less spoilage, but this would have been of no use without the produce to transport.

For the purposes of this book, an agricultural tractor is defined as a machine which, supplied with a suitable fuel, is or was capable of doing useful work pulling, pushing or powering a number of different implements or attachments. Most of an agricultural tractor's work is done with crops, or the soil they grow in, in the course of a typical farming year.

This definition will allow us to concentrate on agricultural tractors. As we follow their story through the course of the book, we will discover why many farmers stuck to horses instead of buying early tractors, as well as other twists to the story.

Steam engines were the first mechanical power seen on many farms. A few firms had a go at building steam-powered tractors but mainly we will discover why users were happy to replace steam with tractors.

The arrival of cars, lorries and vans certainly transformed life on the farm, but mostly they did their work away from the farm itself. Mind you, it is amusing to consider how farmers modified them into tractors, when they got their hands on used examples.

Civil engineering plant hardly fits our definition, but again you might be surprised at how farmers made use of older machines. You might also be surprised at how agricultural tractors got built into construction plant.

Most self-propelled specialist machines fall outside our definition, but they were often affected by tractor design, as you will see.

Thanks to the efforts of private collectors, examples still exist of most of the tractors you will see featured in this book. Often they are restored to working condition. They can be seen in museums, at vintage rallies, working demonstrations and ploughing matches.

When you have read the book, come and see the real thing! As you will discover, they have a fascinating history.

To cover every development in every model would be an impossible task in one book. Luckily the tractor preservation world has many enthusiastic authors, who have researched individual makes or even models. Overleaf there is a list of some recommended authors and titles for those of you who want more specific information.

The most important person is missing from this picture! Pictured in 1977 are two partners and the General Manager of Eaton Tractor Co, joined by the Fiat's General Manager, its local salesman and Service Manager. All they needed to keep them prosperous was a farmer willing to part with plenty of money to buy a tractor (in this case a Fiat 120C)! Throughout this book we will see the varied approaches taken by manufacturers to get that all important order for their tractor. *RLM*

FINDING OUT MORE

No one book can cover your favourite specific make as fully as you might wish. To present an overall picture, some specific exceptions to broad statements have been ignored. There are bound to be odd examples around of tractors built or sold outside the dates given, but the information should be accurate for the majority of production. However, dates quoted need to be treated with caution. Many farmers have always been reluctant to buy the replacement model and others usually bought second-hand so the actual dates a tractor was in regular use will vary widely from farm to farm. The chapters in this book, however, roughly correspond to the periods of major changes.

Having read this book, you may wish to find out more about vintage tractors.

BOOKS

For more colour illustrations of tractors, both historical and modern, try *Tractors in Colour* by Alan C. Butcher, published by Ian Allan, which together with this book, should enable you to identify most tractors that might catch your interest.

Various specialist booksellers can be encountered at rallies, working events and agricultural shows. Many offer a mail order service as well. Titles available will vary according to what is currently in print, but you might find the following names worth bearing in mind.

Publications from author/publisher Allan T. Condie concentrate on the machine(s) featured in each title. Allan has probably done more original research on tractor topics covering more makes than anyone else. Like Allan, the late Charles Cawood of Pocklington, Yorkshire, was an early chairman of the NVTEC and a knowledgeable writer. His family still runs Cawoods Books. The American Society of Agricultural Engineers has published a number of very detailed histories of individual manufacturers, obviously biased towards the American perspective. Charles Wendel has assembled some very well researched specific histories of makes, as well as contributing knowledgeable text to illustrated books. These are usually published by Crestline or Motorbooks. Maurice Sanders writes with first-hand knowledge on timber extraction. Michael Williams writes with a more British perspective, as does Nick Baldwin. Farming Press publishes mainly technical agricultural books but also lists some well-researched one-make histories by different authors. Individual specialist booksellers often come up with other unexpected finds, self-published or locally published, so it is always worth taking time to examine their entire display. Unpromising covers can sometimes conceal fascinating stories. In the second-hand bookshops look out for A. G. Street (good on horses and agricultural background to novels), Ralph Wightman (good on Dorset rural life) and Adrian Bell (father of Martin Bell MP) on Suffolk in the Depression. Reprints of instruction books and manuals can supply much technical information; try booksellers as above. Cawoods and B. J. Sims Publishing offer a particularly extensive range.

VIDEO

Videoscene of Slimbridge, Glos, has been recording modern and vintage agricultural machinery since the early 1980s. The sleeve notes give a good guide to the contents of a specific video. Primetime, and Farming Press, mentioned above, publish some interesting titles. The specialist booksellers previously mentioned all find other interesting titles to fill their range.

16MM FILM

These were made to be watched by a knowledgeable audience. Unlike a video, they are seen at their best when projected onto a screen in the special atmosphere of an audience. Each projection shortens a film's life expectancy, so they can only make rare appearances. The author has been collecting 16mm film featuring agricultural engineering among other topics for over 20 years. His 'Dustbin Film Shows' are so called because most of the films were discarded before being rescued. Other collectors put on occasional film shows, which are also well worth looking out for. The feedback from an interested audience usually adds surprising extra information by the end of a show.

Fitting a 'Leopard' diesel engine would transform the characteristics of the Fordson N. That was the claim of Perkins Diesels when it exhibited this conversion at the 1937 Royal Show. Another 10 years were to pass before any significant conversion sales were made. Once in its stride, this one company transformed British agriculture's approach to the diesel engine. Frank Perkins set a very high standard and the conversion kit is very tidily engineered. Ten years later, electric starting was normal. That starting handle looks hard work on a cold morning! *Ian Allan Library*

Magazines

Old Glory is a monthly magazine available from newsagents; you may need to order it. Tractors are included within its broader coverage of vintage topics. *Vintage Tractor* from Allan T. Condie is well informed and knowledgeable on the topics featured. *Farmers Weekly* is aimed primarily at modern agriculture and is worth reading to see how different modern equipment is; it does carry a small amount of classified vintage advertising each week. *profi*, an English edition of a German machinery magazine, covers modern tractors in thorough detail. Local weekly papers and free advertising publications can lead you to local events and preservation possibilities for sale. The recently launched *Tractor & Machinery* contains reports of sales and events.

Steam Heritage Museums and Rally Guide (TEE Publishing, Warwickshire), published in March each year, tells you what's on where and when. Its museums section gives you an idea of what you will find, when it is open, and has proved pretty reliable. Carried in the car, this has led me to the discovery of many interesting collections. It is worth confirming entries by phone before a special journey, in case of changes since compilation. *Old Glory* offers a similar guide. Try local tourist offices for details of nearby events and collections.

Rally, Working Event, Ploughing Match, Country Working, Steam Rally

Any of the above titles could lead you to an event with vintage tractors present. The description 'NTET approved' denotes a well-run steam rally which is usu-

ally supported by a good selection of tractors. Depending on the event, you may find stalls including specialist booksellers, vintage cars and commercials, military vehicles, stationary engines, crafts, parts for sale and demonstrations. Usually these events are held on farmland, so conditions underfoot are affected by the weather, and some of these events are big, so expect a fair amount of walking. If you are interested in a particular tractor, why not have a chat with the exhibitor? Most are happy to tell you about their exhibit. At most rallies exhibits are roped off for the safety of visitors. The ropes are there for your protection, so please respect them. Please do *not* put youngsters on tractors unless invited to do so. Usually the exhibitor has invested a lot of time and effort into a restoration, so is entitled to appear fussy. Most important though is to enjoy your visit. Old folks — even those who appear rather withdrawn — enjoy such events for the memories they bring back. Try it; you might be delighted at the recollections unlocked.

Most tractors belong to individual collectors, so are not normally on display. Good collections are housed at the Science Museum's reserve store at Wroughton, Wilts; this can be seen only on occasional open days but is well worth the special trip. Stapehill Abbey in the New Forest is the unexpected current home of one of the most important private collections assembled. Toddington Manor in Bedfordshire also features an important display. Probably the best library of written information is at the University of Reading Museum of Rural Life.

Clubs and Get-togethers

More people than you may realise share an interest in old tractors. The National Vintage Tractor & Engine Club consists of over 30 locally based groups meeting around the country, together with other members who

With other makers bringing out new models, David Brown was not to be left out. Its 900 represented the start of a look that would last through several model changes. Gone was the rounded front, to be replaced by a square, more purposeful look. One surprise was the decision to paint the wheels and grille blue. Launched in 1956 it was still recognisably a David Brown. The engine was built up on a sturdy, cast iron base and, just as important, it still *sounded* like a David Brown. *Ian Allan Library*

do not yet have a regular meeting convenient for them. All get the quarterly magazine *Vaporising*. Featuring news, forthcoming events and the eagerly-studied free sales and wants advertising, it is posted direct to each member. Free advertising for members attracts many adverts that would not appear in a publication that charged for them. Typical meetings feature a speaker on a preservation topic, plus plenty of time to catch up with the local news. Laughter is frequently heard. Members range from the slightly interested to the deeply committed and they all make a worthwhile contribution to proceedings. Ring 01454 321010 for a contact address for your local group. Independent tractor clubs range from informal gatherings to well-established and respected clubs. Your local library may be able to point you in the right direction.

Could you own an old tractor? Probably yes. Many enthusiasts have restored tractors in the garden of a town house. Many types will fit into a domestic garage. Practical advice, assistance, sources of spare parts and physical help can be found through your local club. Happiness has been defined as being totally absorbed in what you are doing to the exclusion of all external worries. That state is well known to restorers. Take and keep plenty of photographs if you start a project. They will remind you how much you have already achieved and they have helped many younger enthusiasts obtain the job or training they wanted.

The sources mentioned above have been consulted, among many others, in preparing this book. Despite this, all mistakes you find are all my own work! All comments, feedback, unanswered questions, disagreement or sources of new information are welcome. Write to Jim Wilkie, PO Box 1705, Yate, Bristol BS37 6RF or ring 01454 321010.

PICTURE CREDITS

The Ian Allan Library has been a useful source of pictures: many of these photographs originally appeared in *Modern Transport* magazine

Ray Bird is a talented wildlife photographer who captures the occasional tractor at work as part of his beat.

RLM, Richard Lee Magazines, publishes specialist magazines for the agricultural machinery trade.

RASE is the Royal Agricultural Society of England, best known for the Royal Show, held each year at the beginning of July. It is well worth a visit to see modern agriculture, including tractors, at its best.

The Royal Agricultural College is the oldest of the agricultural colleges. It is based at Cirencester, Glos.

Corinium is the combined photographic collection of the Corinium Museum, Cirencester, and the Countryside Collection at Northleach, Glos.

Agco is the parent company of Massey Ferguson and is still proud of its heritage.

Mike Perkin is a typical enthusiast who enjoys digging up nuggets of unexpected information.

National Motor Museum, Beaulieu; although tractors may seem removed from motor cars, its photographic library came up with some surprises.

Mike Fisher, designer of the SMMOT, confirmed its existence with a photograph.

The rest of the pictures are the author's, taken at different times or from his collection, acquired from various sources.

1. WORLD WAR 1 AND BEFORE, 1901-19

Farmer Charles Hall knew what was needed. 'There appear to be many agricultural operations to which a light yet powerful motor, obtainable at a reasonable cost, may be applied with the advantage of greater economy and rapidity over horse power.' So he wrote in 1901 in the *Journal of the Royal Agricultural Society of England*.

This was pretty forward-looking stuff. Motor cars were still the notoriously unreliable playthings of the rich; an interesting novelty but little more. It was all they could do to drag themselves and their passengers along. Portable steam engines were available to drive threshing machines. Indeed some of the more progressive threshing contractors were able to tow with them as well. That saved using a team of horses to drag the threshing machine from farm to farm. Even so, few could see the horse ever being replaced.

With hindsight, there were the first signs of change in the countryside. Steam traction engines have been mentioned. There were a few sets of Fowler ploughing engines about. These hauled a plough to and fro, using winches mounted under their boilers. Even today a ploughing engine at work is an impressive sight. At the turn of the century a pair was pretty advanced technology.

The first new offering for power farming came from Saundersons of Elstow, which exhibited in 1902 a 'Portable Wind Motor'. This unlikely contrivance was a portable windmill which could be used to drive machinery or its own road wheels, so that it could slowly propel itself along. As a tractor it was useless. Elsewhere in Bedfordshire a Biggleswade cycle manufacturer had other ideas. Dan Albone was working away at nothing less than an agricultural revolution.

The Royal Show, Park Royal, London, was chosen

An early Ivel demonstration in Cumbria drew a typically interested crowd Some came to look at a way of relieving labour for farms. Others came to convince themselves that tractors would never catch on. *Author's Collection*

 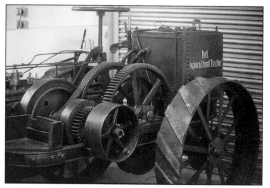

Above and above right: With the guards removed, the simple but sturdy construction of the Ivel can be seen. The belt pulley shaft is connected to the engine by a cone clutch. The reduction gears and chain drive are mounted well clear of dirt. The whole is supported by a sturdy channel steel frame. Big coolant pipes ensure a good circulation of water between the engine and the water tank at the rear. With no previous tractor to form the basis of his design, Dan Albone did an excellent design job. The 6V battery is a later addition. *Author's Collection*

Below: When ground conditions were unsuitable for field work, the International Titan could still be used for road haulage. Delivering grain to the local town used to be a wagoner's day out. The driver would have needed help unloading and with braking the trailers on hills, so the tractor and wagons seen here needed more manpower, but it relieved two horse teams of a hard day's work. *Author's Collection*

for the first showing of his 'Ivel' Agricultural Motor. The RASE judges were most impressed with its potential. The horizontally opposed, two-cylinder 14hp engine ran at 800rpm and was linked to the two drive wheels by a Renolds chain drive to an intermediate shaft. Even with some wheelslip the outfit worked at over 3mph. A single lever controlled the two clutches for forward and reverse travel. The machine weighed 30cwt (1,540kg) and imposed 22.5cwt (1,200kg) on the rear wheels.

Interestingly, one judge felt that more ballast could be needed for some jobs to improve the grip. He saw an 'Ivel' lose grip pulling a miller's cart through slippery ground. He also saw it pulling a three-furrow plough in light soil.

It is difficult to overstate the leap into the unknown that Dan Albone had made. There were a few stationary engines about but self-propelled vehicles were still rare. Yet he set himself the task of producing a self-propelled vehicle with enough power to pull an implement and to do useful work.

Above: **This Hornsby Ackroyd hot bulb, semi-diesel engine, producing 14hp, was built in 1906 and spent 60 years as the standby power unit in a Lincolnshire mill. While this model was not suitable as a tractor engine, it does emphasise that compression ignition engines have been around much longer than many people realise. When exhibited at the Great Dorset Steam Fair in 1997, it still ran delightfully smoothly.** *Author's Collection*

What is still particularly impressive are some of the features of the design. The water tank for cooling was set over the rear axle where its weight was most useful in helping grip. The drive chain had enough sideways flex to allow the cone clutch to operate freely. Although the drives were exposed, they were high up and away from the wheels. There was less risk of picking up stones than in later American designs. Remember, this tractor was built and on sale four years before Henry Ford even started to look at the problem of building a tractor. It was to be 15 years before Ford started commercial production! Had Dan Albone not died in 1906 aged only 46, many more developments could have been expected.

Saunderson & Gifkins, whose short-lived, unlikely wind motor has been mentioned, made the jump to serious tractor manufacture. Based at Elstow in Bedfordshire, they would be aware of the 'Ivel' being produced at nearby Biggleswade. Their designs were crude but effective. From the beginning they used radiators for cooling. A long wheelbase meant there was room to mount a wooden toolbox in front of the radiator (an early form of front weight?).

Saunderson tractors were produced in small numbers. Despite various financial problems, they remained in production between 1904 and 1924. Finally the company was sold to Crossley of Manchester.

In Britain very few steam engines were ever used for direct haulage on the land. They were considered too heavy and to cause too much damage to the soil structure. In drier parts of the world the soil could take more weight and steam traction was used to a limited extent.

Top: Early days with a new tractor meant a worrying time in 1916. With nothing better available, a horse plough has been chained on. Despite his valiant efforts, the ploughman must have been displeased with his work. Exhaust fumes, noise and dust from the International Mogul made his task more difficult.
Corinium Museum, Cirencester

Above: Big country needed big tractors. These all spent their working lives in Saskatchewan, Canada. Their main jobs would have been breaking and ploughing the prairies and driving a separator (threshing drum). This view, showing machines from the 1910-16 period, shows part of the reserve collection at the Western Development Museum. *Author's Collection*

A major disadvantage of steam, however, was the need for large quantities of water as well as coal.

Petrol came in returnable cans or steel barrels. Fuelling for a day's work merely involved pouring a few gallons into the fuel tank. However, the increased risk of fire was often used as an argument against petrol engines.

As early as 1904 Dan Albone had demonstrated an alternative carburettor, enabling a farmer to run his 'Ivel' on paraffin (kerosene). Despite the higher cost per gallon, many tractors continued to be made to run on straight petrol. The justification was that this avoided many of the problems that would plague paraffin tractors.

A paraffin engine still had to be started on petrol. Heat from the exhaust pipe was used to preheat the mixture before it got into the cylinder. If the tractor was not working hard, the engine could gradually cool down. Eventually the paraffin could not evaporate properly. As well as diluting the lubricating oil, power would decrease rapidly, with white smoke of unburnt paraffin coming from the exhaust. Shortly, damp paraffin would settle on the tip of the spark plug causing misfiring and the engine would stop.

To prevent this cooling down, some of the earlier tractors had a cooling system that was barely adequate. The tractor usually ran hot. It was intended that the cooling water could boil away and that this evaporation would aid cooling.

This was assisted by water injection. If the engine got too hot, the first symptom was a knocking noise caused by the fuel mixture exploding before being ignited by the spark. Apart from hammering the engine components with shock loads, it caused a rapid fall off in power. On some early designs, opening a small valve allowed a water spray to be drawn into the inlet manifold. This cooled the mixture down. The spray was set so that no knock could be heard. Part of the effect was the water turning to steam in the cylinder. On later designs, when radiators became more efficient, they were often blanked off by a radiator blind or shutters to keep the engine's operating temperature up.

To enter a 1909 War Office trial, Hornsby of Lincoln produced an oil engined tractor. Following its outstanding performance, Hornsby added tracks to produce what was the world's first crawler. Despite commissioning a sales film, there were almost no orders. However, the American company Holt did agree to pay £4,000 for the American and Canadian patent rights. Holt carried on development work and later became a major constituent of the Caterpillar Company, which is still building crawlers today. It certainly got good value for its modest investment!

A competitive trial was held in Winnipeg, Canada, in 1910. The main objective was to find tractors to break prairie soil. International Harvester sent along a Titan Type D. This was very different from the Titan later to be seen in Britain. Weighing in at just under 10 tons, it developed 45bhp. It pulled a 10-furrow plough, which carried a crew of three men riding on the plough to raise and lower individual furrows as required.

While it did well in the trial, International only built four in 1910, increasing production to 186 in 1911. Tractors of that size were of no application in Britain. International Harvester had been formed in 1902 by the merger of McCormick and Deering, both big makers of binders. Tractor production for them seemed a logical extension of their range.

Marshalls of Gainsborough built its massive, oil engined 'Colonial' models aimed at the same market. This was a very forward looking move from a Lincolnshire company more used to steam power.

The most fraught part of an early tractor driver's day was getting his charge started. With maximum exertion a tractor driver could generate perhaps one third of a horsepower. Would that, plus cunning and intelligence, be sufficient to persuade a ton or more of cold, stubborn engine into action?

Getting petrol into the cylinders was only half the battle. The other vital ingredient was the spark. When that was present and correct at full strength, starting was more likely. The trouble was that all sorts of enemies were poised to sap its strength. Turning the engine slowly weakened the spark. Damp on the body of the magneto, the plug leads, or a plug could reduce the voltage.

Even before any attempt at starting, many lubrication points would need attention with an oil can. Oil levels would want checking and replenishing. Possibly there would be a rotary lubricator to be filled, ready to dispense regular drops of oil to crucial bearing points.

Many drivers were injured attempting to start tractors: sprains, bruising and broken limbs were typical injuries right up to the development of reliable electric starters. Drivers even died attempting to start their

tractors: typical causes were heart attacks, entanglements with the flywheel, or being crushed or run over after starting in gear. No wonder most tractors were laid up for the winter!

The start of World War 1 in 1914 meant there was an upsurge in demand for the output from farms. Inevitably many of the youngest and fittest employees went away in the forces. Other employees were attracted away to better paid jobs with contractors building new army camps or manufacturing munitions. Many of the best horses were requisitioned for military requirements. Stacks of hay were commandeered to feed them.

Suddenly a farm could find itself short of both horses and feed for replacements, even if they could be bought. These shortages led more farmers to consider whether a tractor could improve their situation.

To help their thinking the Highland & Agricultural Society organised a simple working demonstration at Stirling. The tractors that took part illustrated the bewildering choice that faced a first-time tractor buyer. From America came the International Harvester Mogul 8-16 and the Overtime, which was the forerunner of the John Deere range. Heavy advertising meant these were the better known makes. Both models featured a basic stationary engine mounted on a channel steel frame. They proved able to pull the available ploughs, drove a threshing machine, and hauled 5 tons on the road at about 3mph.

The Mogul was found the more manoeuvrable. The main criticisms noted were occasional 'violent explosions in the silencer, which appeared to indicate that some adjustment was required'. Preserved Moguls *still* display this alarming habit! A Bull tractor was entered but 'could not be sent forward for demonstration' by the importers.

In 1917 reports of a tractor at work would draw an interested, if sceptical, crowd. Tackling a steam engine's job, like this new International Titan driving a threshing drum, would be even more unusual. The Army corporal would be the driver, as some Titans came under military control. *Corinium Museum, Cirencester*

Smaller and lighter than a steam engine, the International Titan 10-20 was nearly as powerful for most jobs. For the last 20 years of its working life this Titan was used as a road roller for farm track repairs, before being rescued and restored by Dave Wilkins, seen driving. Dave normally works on state-of-the-art New Holland machinery but enjoys the contrasting challenge of restoring and running the Titan. *Author's Collection*

Steam was a possibility to consider. Manns of Hunslet, Leeds, put forward its Light Steam Tractor, weighing in at just over 5 tons. It hauled a four-furrow plough with ease, burning about 1cwt of coal per acre. Again the threshing machine presented no problems and neither did hauling a 6-ton load, as it was fitted with road springs. The judges liked its reliability and felt that depreciation would be low. Even so, at £465 it was £200 dearer than a Mogul and it needed 200gal of water every 4hr. This would imply another farm employee, horse and water cart needed most of the time for water carrying.

The cheapest entry was the Wyles Motor Plough. A simple two-wheeled design, it was steered by an operator from behind at the end of a pair of long handles. Controlling a machine weighing over a ton must have needed a strong chap on the handle bars, although

either wheel could be declutched to give a form of power steering. Indeed the judges felt it was 'easy and safe to handle'. They were very impressed with the work done and felt it was 'well designed on sound practical lines'. Rather surprisingly, the Wyles proved the only tractor able to cope with the steeper slopes while ploughing at full depth. With hindsight this design was probably benefiting from weight transfer from the plough.

The transmission arrangement was very ingenious and enabled the plough to run level even with one wheel in the furrow. A ratchet and pawl provided a simple power lift for the plough. With an 11hp engine it was not sufficiently powerful to drive a threshing drum but was suitable for lighter jobs. With a stabiliser wheel added it could pull a binder. The judges 'have confidence in recommending this implement to farmers as being well suited to do good work on moderate sized farms'.

With ground conditions firm and no rain, the tractors happened to be working under near ideal conditions. Apart from the Wyles, all were still unable to plough the steeper parts of the field due to lack of wheel grip. One wonders if the judges would have been so favourably impressed if the trial had been held in a wet November.

No British motor tractors were forwarded, 'as the factories were engaged in military contracts'.

Probably the main lesson of the trial was that under

Above: **Henry Ford driving his first prototype agricultural
tractor in 1907. Ford was an engineer long before becoming
a businessman. Nothing gave him greater pleasure than
tinkering with and improving machinery. Perhaps wisely,
Ford concentrated on getting his Model T car into
production before finalising his tractor design.** *RASE*

Left: **The Ford Model T was the first mass produced car.
Several firms offered conversions to make them into
tractors. While this was a short-lived trend, it was a
sensible approach. Most of the components used were
cheap and well proven. In fact, you could say this was the
forerunner of the later specialist converters. As the Model
T had an epicyclic transmission, you could even claim
these were the first tractors with change on-the-move gearboxes!** *Author's Collection*

Below: **Like all Model T conversions, the Eros was
intended to provide a low-cost tractor. In 1918 it was
unusual to buy a motor car of any description. It must
have required an act of faith to start modifying it so
drastically.** *Author's Collection*

favourable circumstances a tractor could replace missing men and horses on farms that could afford the outlay. It was clear that tractor power was needed. With
British factories on a war footing, it made sense to bring
in well-proven tractors from the United States. The
International Titan was a twin-cylinder version of the
Mogul. About 3,000 of these were imported for use by
the War Agricultural Executive Committees to increase
food production.

Trials like this demonstrated that a designer could
not be satisfied designing a tractor just as good as one

already on the market. He had to chase a constantly changing target.

When Dan Albone was designing the 'Ivel' tractor his target was the horse. He built a tractor that could do rather more work than two horses but did not get tired. It needed new skills from the operator. It could keep on going when horses would have stopped. When the 'Ivel' was not required it could be left in a shed and did not require daily feeding and grooming. After Dan Albone's death the company lost momentum, yet it made many overseas sales. It was some years before the 'Ivel' was clearly outclassed by competitors. As sales fell away, the company's fortunes declined. By 1916 it was an importer and it failed in 1921.

The designers of the International Mogul and Titan and the Overtime were working on the same assump-

The end of the production line at the original Brady Street plant in 1917. The Fordson name has just started to appear on the radiator. These are changing from open sides to solid sided. Ford's delay in going ahead with his first tractor permitted starting with a much more robust design. *RASE*

tions. Their tractors could replace horse or mule teams on American farms. With the outbreak of World War 1 it was relatively easy to build a few thousand more of the existing design and ship them over to Britain. There they could be sold to farmers and the Government anxious to replace labour and horses needed for the fighting.

Other British importers sourced alternative products aimed at the American market. Almost regardless of quality, some firm in Britain would order a few to try and sell them at a profit. Thus even tractors with a suspect reputation in the United States turned up in Britain with one important feature — immediate delivery. Inevitably these would find a buyer who needed a tractor urgently. Both Herbert Austin and Harry Ferguson had to cope with the consequences of this. Austin imported various dubious makes; Ferguson had some allocated to his control while responsible for tractors in Ireland. Both felt inspired to design better tractors than the ones they had.

Listed in contemporary publications was what looked like the answer to British requirements. The 'Ideal' tractor was built at Hednesford, Staffordshire, with a 35hp engine and a mounted four-furrow plough. The

linkage that carried it appeared to be operated by a hand winch. A 'Power Take Off' is described, to drive mowers and binders, as well as a mounted 7ft 6in cut mower; both axles were sprung.

The only contemporary illustration shows a tidy looking design. The technical innovations would be 'invented' once again years later by other, better known, makers. Presumably there were faults in the design and the makers did not have the resources to meet the needs of the British Government. None the less, the 'Ideal' demonstrated that technical innovation, on its own, is not enough to produce a commercially successful tractor.

Henry Ford was the right man in the right place. He had already proved that he could produce the Model T Ford car and truck in vast quantities. Indeed, kits were being offered by other manufacturers to convert them into crude tractors. He already had a prototype that looked promising. In fact, he offered to commence immediate manufacture in Britain.

Later it was agreed instead that production would start in Detroit. Henry Ford was as good as his word, shipping the first of 5,000 tractors before the end of 1917.

Britain got much needed tractors, but Ford got production under way when American farmers were still prospering. Once the British Government order was fulfilled, Ford could sell all the tractors he could make. Unlike other contemporary tractors, the transmission was fully enclosed, so the potential for wear was reduced.

The 'Fordson' (Ford & Son) name was adopted as speculators had already registered a 'Ford Tractor Co'. What ensured sales was the low price of the Fordson. Mass production meant that Ford could turn them out in vast quantities, reducing the cost per tractor.

Anxious not to profit from a war of which he disapproved, Ford shipped his first tractors to the Ministry of Munitions to be loaned out to British farmers.

To get the best from the available tractors, many were operated under Government supervision. The two main models were Titans and the new Fordson, sometimes referred to as the 'MoM tractor'.

Much of Britain's food was imported. When submarines threatened merchant shipping, Britain started to fear food shortages. Food production was encouraged; farmers responded to the stimulus.

Solemn pledges were given that wartime prices would continue.

Engineering works had expanded during the war and now faced the end of major military contracts. Producing tractors seemed a sensible new development. Agriculture was booming. They would be bound to meet a strong demand. Nothing could go wrong, could it?

One American make that did not reach British shores when new in 1917 was the Allwork. This example would have been imported much more recently. It featured the cross engine layout that later was favoured by Case in the 1920s. The Allwork's builder, the Electric Wheel Co, later specialised in supplying wheels to agricultural machinery manufacturers. *Author's Collection*

2. PEACE AND HARD TIMES, 1919-30

With peace and with the British Government order fulfilled, Ford could sell all the tractors it could make. Henry Ford's aim was to pay men well and plan their work, so that, working efficiently, they could produce a larger number of components per shift. He recognised costs per vehicle could be brought down by mass production.

Not foreseeing this competition, various makers committed themselves to producing tractors in Britain. The Glasgow was a three-wheel-drive tractor with two front-driven wheels and a single at the rear. Manufacturing was in a former Scottish munitions factory. Launched with high hopes, production soon tailed off due to lack of orders.

Alldays & Onions was a well-respected Birmingham firm of engineers. Its tractor was built up on a channel steel chassis with a substantial belt pulley on the offside. The four-cylinder engine developed 30hp and a drawbar pull of 2,000lb.

While an excellent tractor for its day, its high price meant it failed to sell. It could have replaced a traction engine. Unfortunately, second-hand traction engines were relatively cheap, with many being released from military service.

A typical rural Ford dealer would handle cars, vans and tractors. Many potential customers would have had dealings with them long before buying their first Fordson tractor. A later façade has been built onto the traditional half-timbered building of J. E. Chappell and Co at High Street, Odiham, Hants, photographed in the mid-1950s when such premises were still to be found. *National Motor Museum*

Above left: **An impressive turnout drawn to a 1921 ploughing match. Organised by Bridges of Cirencester, the majority of the tractors are the recently introduced International Junior model, but there are quite a number of Titans and Moguls. Only one driver elected to try his luck with a Fordson. These tractors would have made their way to the match by road at not much more than walking pace, so would have come from a fairly compact area.** *Corinium Museum, Cirencester*

Above: **Pitching hay was hard work on a hot day. A towed hay loader saved the work but was very hard on the horses pulling both the wagon and the drag of the loader. A device called the Iron Horse was fitted into the wagon shafts to convert it to a crude draw bar. With an International 10-20 attached, only the two chaps on the load have to work hard. Once loaded, the Iron Horse would be detached to allow a 'proper' horse to take the load back to the stack.** *Corinium Museum, Cirencester*

Left: **The International Junior was a first response to the Fordson. By means of a modified drawbar, two horse-drawn drills could be pulled at once. The four-cylinder engine with rear-mounted radiator was also used on International's trucks. There is a curious mystery about this photograph. The negative has been defaced to conceal that a second man is riding on the other drill. His 'remains' have been left clutching a control lever. Presumably it was to suggest only one man was needed on the drill pair.** *Corinium Museum, Cirencester*

Above: Herbert Austin had been involved in marketing imported tractors during World War 1. With peace, he felt that he could produce something similar to the Fordson but British built. Finding he could not compete on price, production was later transferred to France, where import taxes gave protection. *Author's Collection*

Below: The Fowler ploughing engine represented the first successful attempt to mechanise cultivations. Unlike a tractor, it remained at a headland and pulled the implement in towards itself, using the large underslung winch. The trouble was, it needed a matching engine to pull the implement back. Only one of the pair could be doing useful work at a time. They could travel under their own power and pull a load. This was usually no more than an implement out of work, a living van or a water carrier. By contrast, a tractor pulled its own implement and could be used on its own. When offered a realistic choice most farmers, and contractors, gave up steam in favour of tractors. *Author's Collection*

Herbert Austin, the motor manufacturer, had been involved with importing tractors for the British Government during the war. What he saw encouraged him to add a tractor to the cars he was manufacturing. His design offered few advantages over a Fordson and at a higher cost. Manufacture was soon transferred to France, where high customs duties offered a protected home market.

While Ford's low prices were causing problems in Britain, the situation was little different in the United States. Smaller manufacturers found themselves unable to compete. Even General Motors took fright at Ford's prices and ceased production of their Samson, having only recently bought the company.

International fought back, cutting prices. It was staying in the tractor business. Its designers were set to work to produce Fordson beaters. Although not often seen in Britain, it also made much bigger tractors than the Fordson, which helped. Its direct competitor was the newly introduced 8-16 Junior, but that still had external chain drive. Its first effective response was the 15-30, launched in 1921.

Like the Fordson it had a fully enclosed cast-iron frame. The engine had overhead valves and ball-race main bear-

Left: **This Minneapolis demonstrates why so many unusual tractors in preservation originate from Canada. Most of the time in the Prairies the weather is either hot and dry or very cold. This reduces the rusting problem. With little profit to be made from scrap, many farms tend to accumulate discarded tractors. With strong local demand at the time, no attempt was made to export this cross-engined model in Europe.** *Author's Collection*

Below: **More examples of tractors conserved by the Canadian Prairie climate, where machinery can stand outside for years with minimal deterioration. No doubt by now some in this line-up have been restored. The front row are typical products of the late 1920s and early 1930s while those in the back row were produced in the early 1940s.** *Author's Collection*

Above: The Wallingford trials attracted a comprehensive selection of current tractors in 1930. The International Farmall entry featured the tricycle layout, which demonstrated that a row crop tractor can undertake ploughing. With no front wheel in the furrow, the driver must have had to concentrate on his steering. *Ian Allan Library*

Right: The International 10-20 was suffering from wheel-spin (to judge by the wheelmarks from the previous pass) so was obviously being worked hard. Although rated at 10 drawbar horsepower it was found to put out 17hp on test. This may explain how it gained its enviable reputation and 10 years of commercial success. *Ian Allan Library*

ings for greater fuel efficiency. The transmission was more efficient than Ford's worm final drive. A major innovation was offering a power take off. This could be used to drive towed implements for certain jobs like mowing or pulling a binder. This offered a significant improvement in working. The 15-30 meant that International could meet Fordson head on by offering a stronger and more technically advanced tractor. The similar but cheaper and smaller 10-20, introduced in 1923, was more than a match for Fordson in performance.

By 1930 International had the Farmall in production. This was a completely new class of tractor. A high clear-

Above left: **Blackstone entered what was effectively an International 15-30, modified to take its diesel engine. With the financial troubles of AGE, no more was heard of this development.** *Ian Allan Library*

Left: **AEC built this Rushton, which had tracks by Roadless Traction. While cheaper than an equivalent Caterpillar, the judges commented unfavourably on the loss of power when steering.** *Ian Allan Library*

Below: **Entered by McLaren, the Dieselsclepper was built by Mercedes-Benz. The fuel system suffered a stoppage and it consumed large amounts of water. Not much was heard of this model afterwards.** *Ian Allan Library*

Top: **Heaviest entry was the Caterpillar Sixty. Weighing in at over 9 tons, it developed 60hp at the drawbar. Starting was by flicking the flywheel with a crowbar.** *Ian Allan Library*

Above: **Despite not entering production, the Aveling & Porter was a significant entry. Its high-speed diesel acquitted itself so well that when the company folded, designer Frank Perkins was bold enough to launch his own company: Perkins Engines of Peterborough.** *Ian Allan Library*

Right: **The Latil featured four-wheel drive and four-wheel steering. With suspension and a 17mph top speed, it was a dual purpose machine. Although running on high pressure pneumatic tyres, extra grip could be obtained by the aid of folding spuds which gave more bite. In practice, most Latils went for industrial purposes or for timber haulage.** *Ian Allan Library*

ance was provided for mounting implements underneath. Adjustable wheel spacings enabled them to fit between rows of growing crops. Farmalls inspired other makers to come up with their interpretation of a row crop tractor. When Britain needed tractors to cope with potato crops during World War 2, American makers had a good choice available.

While International went for improved product quality, a most surprising company took a much less enterprising route. Merely trying to match the Fordson with a British-built tractor was the approach of AEC. Its Rushton was so similar that early production tractors were said to use some Fordson components. AEC's timing was bad with farming depressed, but presumably it was trying to offset a decline in bus and lorry sales. This was a tractor that offered too little and was launched too late.

Fifteen years later, unintentionally, AEC produced what many timber men would later consider the ideal timber tractor. This was the four-wheel drive AEC Matador artillery tractor.

It is one thing to offer tractors for sale, but it is often more difficult to find customers willing to buy them. Here the situation was very mixed. Farmers' sons and others had returned from a mechanised war. They were keen to adopt mechanical power. The one vital ingredient missing was money.

By 1922 politicians' guarantees had proved worthless, and prices and values fell. It was an early symptom of the decline in world trade that led to the Great Depression.

Farmers went bankrupt and left the farm or reduced costs and sacked men. Fields were left to self-sow to grass. Grazing a few livestock on the land cut expenses, even though there was little prospect of much profit. Some went in for poultry or dairying. This sort of agriculture was despised by 'proper' farmers who resented the routine involved. Those who took it up, especially with a low cost system, were able to stem their losses and perhaps make a small profit.

All these changes in the farming system needed less power. Farmers who still had capital to buy machinery were buying engines and milking machines for the dairy herd. If they needed a motor vehicle, rather than buy a tractor, they could justify a van or lorry to transport milk to the nearest railway station or eggs to town.

With money tight the horse still had some pretty strong advantages. The fuel could be grown on the farm. Unlike a tractor it could breed its replacement. So, many farmers were sticking to the horse.

In the USA, climatic conditions meant farmers had less scope for changing their type of farming. They too economised, however, by not buying replacements for existing tractors and machinery. Events in Russia meant that many orders for agricultural machinery were either cancelled or were never paid for. Manufacturers still committed to steam equipment as their main line found demand drastically reduced.

Manufacturers were losing money. Responses varied but often amalgamation or takeover was the solution. The Agricultural & General Engineering Co (AGE)

Above: **The steering arrangement of the International Farmall F12 allowed a choice of front axles to be specified. The wide axle chosen by this Gloucestershire customer makes ploughing easier than the tricycle layout used at the Wallingford trials. The high and narrow construction gives the driver a good view of the ground between the two axles but the high seating position has put the driver out of easy reach of the plough controls.** *Corinium Museum, Cirencester*

was the biggest British answer. A company promoter convinced a dozen respected firms, albeit most with financial problems, that if they came together, they could revive themselves. Some rationalisation was possible, but the main effect was to hide from managers how serious the situation was getting.

Similar steps were being taken in the United States. Many of what were to become familiar names in the British market were formed or strengthened in this way. Allis Chalmers, Oliver, Massey Harris and Case were some of the more notable examples. Ford took the drastic step of stopping tractor production altogether in 1928. The impact of this change was only slightly reduced by the decision to increase production at Cork in Ireland to meet what demand still existed.

The impact of all these strains on tractor production could be seen clearly at one unique event. The Royal Agricultural Society of England announced that a tractor demonstration would be held in 1930 at Wallingford, Berkshire (now in Oxfordshire). This had the effect of luring out a number of interesting new developments. Several trends proved very significant.

Four British-made diesel tractors ran satisfactorily with fuel costs roughly one third of those of well-proven paraffin tractors. Part of this saving came from the much more efficient use of fuel by a diesel engine. Diesel fuel was also much cheaper, at half the price of tractor paraffin and a third the price of petrol.

On a commercial basis the results were rather more mixed. The Marshall proved to be the forerunner of the Marshall and Field Marshall range, which stayed in production for the next 23 years.

McLaren did not pursue tractor manufacture and instead concentrated on bigger industrial diesel engines, although it did convert some steamers to McLaren diesel power.

Blackstone and Aveling & Porter were both part of AGE. After its crash Blackstone survived, building big industrial diesels, while Aveling was re-formed as Aveling Barford.

The development team of the Aveling & Porter entry would form the nucleus of F. Perkins Diesels at Peterborough. There it later had a major impact on agricultural tractor design.

Mercedes-Benz did not pursue tractor sales in Britain in the 1930s. It did continue to trade and prosper, returning with the Unimog 30 years later.

Another category was the semi-diesel tractor. These machines were very similar to the oil engines built by Hornsby back in 1908 for its tracklayer. They kept running by the effect of an internal hotspot which ignited the fuel when it was injected. This made them much less fussy about fuel quality, although rather thirstier than a full diesel. Low fuel costs meant they were still cheap to run.

The Swedish Munktells were never marketed effectively in Britain. In the late 1970s many Volvo loading shovels built by BM (Bolinder Munktell) Volvo finished their working lives on British farms.

The imposingly named Hofherr Scrantz Clayton Shuttleworth from Budapest later found an appreciative market in Australia, possibly as result of its good showing at the trials. Thirty years later, as Dutra, the same works were to supply a distinctive four-wheel drive tractor for the British market.

With Lanz the story was rather different. In Britain it found a number of farmers that appreciated the combination of rugged construction and fuel economy. Enthusiastic owners claimed the machines would run happily on sump oil or creosote. Indeed, even at the 1939 Royal Show they were still selling well, although the maker's after-sales arrangements were shortly to be disrupted. Hosier Farms in Wiltshire were enthusiastic users for many years. After a break of 30 years, Lanz resumed supplying tractors to Britain as John Deere's German subsidiary.

Caterpillar gave an effective demonstration of the potential of its range of tracklayers. During the fairly searching test only one Caterpillar needed a minor adjustment. Otherwise all five needed no adjustments or repairs.

Even today, the specification of the French Latil sounds quite modern. Although farmers did not buy it, timber merchants recognised a wonderful replacement for the traction engine for timber hauling. Maybe Latil was 40 years ahead of its time for the agricultural market?

The Rushton 'Roadless' tracklayer was to prove a fairly short-lived model, but the Roadless company went on to produce several popular crawlers over the next 30 years.

Transatlantic entries included the three International models. Two Massey Harrises were entered — a 12/20 and a 20/30 — while from Case came a 'C' and an 'L'.

Surprisingly, only one Fordson was entered, an Irish-built example, and it was withdrawn due to a casting fault in the cylinder block. Thus it was that the most significant of all the current tractors was not reported on. The basis of the Fordson's commercial success was that for many farms and jobs, any tractor was better than no tractor.

The Wallingford trials were a watershed. Never again would farmers be offered a chance to compare so many tractors at one location and one time in quite the same way. They confirmed that tractor power was the way forward.

Among all the doom and gloom there were hopeful signs. A few far-sighted farmers were in a position to take advantage of the bad conditions to rent or buy large acreages very cheaply. By cultivating the land cheaply with tractors, they could still make a modest profit even at current prices. They would be the first to admit that their farming was done on the cheap, but at least their land was not lying neglected and unfarmed. Was this to be the way forward?

Below: **The Farmall design left an uncluttered space under the tractor. This was ideal for underslung equipment with a good view down. In this mid-mounted position hoes moved in the same direction as the steering corrections. A skilled driver could work very close to a growing crop without the risk of damage. Independent brakes enabled tight turns to be made on the headlands. On later models, styled sheet metalwork would conceal the steering, improving the tractor's appearance. This successful design inspired other makers to offer an equivalent model.** *Author*

3. THE DEPRESSION YEARS, 1930-39

When Ford stopped tractor production in the United States, Ford of Britain sought a modern manufacturing facility in this country. The request was granted to a far greater extent than was probably expected. A new, fully integrated factory that would be almost totally self sufficient was approved. An expanse of unpromising marshland at Dagenham in Essex was chosen as the site. Construction was rapid, spurred on by Henry Ford's frequent visits to England. (Another purpose of his visits was to locate and purchase exhibits for his new Greenfield Museum, which was partly inspired by the Science Museum. It is interesting to realise that Henry Ford was one of the first collectors of vintage machinery.)

The most remarkable aspect of the construction was that it went on despite the Great Depression and the Wall Street Crash. Henry Ford could be stubborn, but in this case it ensured the plant was built. One of his many prejudices was that he detested accountants. Doubtless, had he heeded their advice, the plant would not have been built. Luckily for Britain, he pressed on. Maybe it was his farming background that encouraged him to take the longer view.

From 1932 to 1947 this one plant would account for the production of the majority of tractors used in Britain, as well as most tractor exports. Besides this it was producing cars, vans and trucks down the same assembly line.

Until the early 1930s horses still enjoyed one big advantage over tractors. They could move from field to road at will. Steel tractor wheels cut into a road surface. Any attempt to pull on to the road would bring complaints and prosecution for damage.

According to tractor makers this was no problem. They offered 'easily fitted' road bands that could be slipped over the cleats for road work. Most road bands were soon discarded and tractors confined to fields.

In the United States Firestone was experimenting with low pressure tyres for tractors. Compared with lorry tyres the sidewalls were much more flexible, so that effectively a much bigger area of tyre was in contact with the ground. Inflation pressure was typically only 10psi, much lower than for other types of tyre.

Agricultural tyres proved the key to the totally versatile tractor that could work in the field *and* on the highway. Once pneumatic tyres were accepted, tractors could be built with a higher top gear for road work.

Pneumatic tyres greatly increased the number of jobs a tractor could tackle. Transport jobs became part of the work undertaken by many tractors. At last, farmers had an outfit that could be sent to the station to collect goods or deliver grain to a local buyer. This provided more work for a tractor in the year and reduced the need for horses.

Makers started to build bigger, rubber-tyred, four-wheel trailers for hauling bigger loads. Even so, there were still jobs where spade lugs gave a better grip and many farms would refit them in winter. With pneumatic tyres established as a sensible alternative, tractor makers started to look at improving their designs to take advantage of the higher speeds that were possible. It was found that inner tubes could be filled with water to add weight. Adding calcium chloride prevented the water freezing.

This tranquil scene is destined for startling change. Pulling a three-furrow Oliver trailer plough, the driver is actually ploughing grassland on part of the new Ford Dagenham site with a Cork-built Fordson. Hidden from the camera, urgent construction work is in progress constructing the giant factory. Prudently, Ford had bought far more land than it thought it would need. The balance was known as Lake Farm and continued to be farmed. The curious profile of the rear mudguard is of interest. A toolbox is incorporated in the reinforced base. If the plough struck an obstacle, Fordsons had a tendency to rear. Should this happen, the toolboxes were intended to hit the ground first, preventing the driver being crushed!
Ian Allan Library

Before 1950 on most arable farms the threshing machine was still the most complex powered machine needed. By replacing a steam traction engine with a rubber-tyred tractor, a threshing contractor needed to send only one man with the outfit. A tractor could be left to run unattended. If the man released was suitable, he could operate an additional tractor and threshing drum if the work was available.

Farmers much preferred to supply paraffin instead of coal and water for a steamer and the fire risk from sparks was reduced in the stackyard. Of course, if the contractor bought a diesel Marshall, then fuel costs were even lower. Not surprisingly, the Marshall proved very popular with threshing contractors, especially as a winch was available as a factory-fitted feature.

Agricultural colleges began to recognise that a knowledge of machinery would be worth while and some instruction on the care and operation of tractors began to figure in courses.

In some cases the design changes resulting from the introduction of pneumatic tyres would cause problems for buyers opting for steel wheels. Some tractors had an arrangement in the gearbox to inhibit selecting top or high gear. This would be set at the factory or by the dealer if steel wheels were specified.

Not all tractors went to replace horses on farms. Industrial tractors on solid tyres or high-pressure pneumatics were used to replace horses on town work. By

Right: Golf clubs were an important early market for tractors. With large areas to be gang mowed, mechanical power was welcome. Several firms specialised in fitting extra reduction axles to lorries to produce tractors for this market. The wide steel wheels offered grip, rolling and slight turf improvement. Pattissons, who made this conversion, are still in business today supplying golf accessories. *Author's Collection*

pulling a number of trailers in turn, one tractor could do the work of several teams of horses.

Harry Ferguson was the moving spirit behind the next major innovation. He had come up with a pretty effective design of plough to fit a Fordson tractor. Besides being light and simple, it stopped the Fordson's dangerous vice of rearing up and over, crushing the driver.

When production of the Fordson tractor stopped in 1928, Ferguson could see his plough sales being affected. He resolved to design his own tractor and plough combination to work as one integrated outfit. This could offer several important advantages. The plough or other implement was carried by the tractor when not in work. In work, the forces of the soil on the plough were transmitted to the back wheels of the tractor. At the same time other forces were holding the front of the tractor down so that it could not rear.

His vision was to build a lightweight tractor and implement that gripped the ground like a heavyweight. A hydraulic oil pump to operate the linkage was included in the design. This gave the driver fingertip control. The final result did nearly everything that Ferguson had hoped. It was light and easy to drive and operate. It outperformed bigger tractors. Once he had persuaded David Brown Gears to start building them, there was only one problem. Farmers would not buy Ferguson Browns.

Two main factors put them off. A Ferguson Brown needed the matching implements. With other tractors they could use existing ones. The other factor was far more difficult to overcome. Farmers simply could not believe their eyes! Here was a tractor being demonstrated doing things which they 'knew' from experience such a small tractor could not do. Being cautious, most kept their hands in their pockets and did not buy. They would let a neighbour try one first.

Disappointed with British sales, Harry Ferguson managed to persuade Henry Ford to start making a tractor in Detroit incorporating the Ferguson system. Ford knew Ferguson from his ploughs and was intrigued by the potential of this new system.

Back in England, 'Young' David Brown felt some of the disappointing sales were due to shortcomings in the design of the Ferguson Brown. He had been anxious to introduce improvements, but Ferguson resisted change. Eventually he was able to buy out Ferguson's tractor interests in Britain and start building tractors to his own design as 'David Browns'.

Curiously, in both cases the results were the same. Two better looking and better performing tractors were launched in 1939. Both had power take offs. Both had hydraulics that could be used even if the tractor was not in gear.

David Brown's incorporated the better engine. Although built as a petrol or paraffin engine, it was always planned that the design would later be used as a diesel. Ford based its engine on a well-proven sidevalve design that could be built on existing machinery.

Left: **Fitting pneumatic tyres would make tractors far more versatile. Firestone was a pioneer and this crowd had gathered in 1934 to see for themselves the difference it made. Only a few balloon tyres were built with such a simple chevron design. The lugs were too small for maximum traction. Importantly, they did prove the idea was commercially feasible. Notice how by sheer chance the Firestone name is at the top of both tyres and picked out in white? You can be sure a lot of meticulous preparation went into setting up this picture.**
Ian Allan Library

Design work on the Ford Ferguson was supervised by Charles Sorensen, who had been responsible for the original Fordson. Input from stylists produced a much more 'finished' design than the Ferguson-Brown.

Harry Ferguson's original assumption was that Ford would produce the Ford Ferguson at Dagenham as well. This was frustrated in two ways. The share structure of Ford of Britain meant it was not bound to follow American orders. (This would not be resolved until 1960 when moves started to bring Ford of Britain fully under US control.) Even more pressingly with the outbreak of World War 2, there was no question of Government permission to halt tractor production for the major upheaval needed to introduce a new model and implements.

Harry Ferguson spent much time in the United States pushing the Ferguson system. He was responsible for selling Ford's entire tractor output through his sales organisation. Enough Ford Fergusons got to Britain to establish a good reputation. Incidentally, the correct designation of the model was a 'Ford tractor with Ferguson system', although they were usually referred to as Ford Fergusons.

Thoughtful farmers could see the risk of war coming closer. So could Ford of Britain, which offered to make 5,000 tractors for the British Government, to be stored at Ford dealers around the country. In the event of war they would be at the Government's immediate disposal. If there was no war before 1940, Ford would take them off the Government's hands at no cost.

By 1939 Dagenham employed 8,000 and accounted for the production of the majority of tractors used in Britain, as well as most tractor exports.

Streamlining was the up-to-date fashion for cars in the mid-1930s. Most American tractor makers carried out related restyling exercises on their tractors. The effect was quite remarkable, as awkward, gawky designs like the Farmall, Allis Chalmers and John Deere emerged as stylish looking, sleek tractors.

Left: **In 1935 Firestone reported that Sir Malcolm Campbell (pictured) 'had written praising the efficiency of the tyres'. He had had his Fordson tractor converted for use on his private golf course at Povey Cross, Surrey. He was reported to be delighted with 'perfect traction' and elimination of damage caused by steel wheels. While the rear tyres are of the original round balloon profile, the fronts displayed another short-lived tread. The wheels are American, built by French & Hecht.** *Ian Allan Library*

Below left: **The same year, Ford introduced a special golf course version of the Fordson with pneumatic tyres and light spoked wheels, rather than the heavy cast iron centres used on agricultural models. It was claimed to pull up to nine mowers and be useful for rolling and harrowing the course. Several examples have survived into preservation. Although advertised as a distinct model, it would cause little disruption during manufacture.** *Ian Allan Library*

Below: **'Costs less than three horses and does the work of eight' was the slogan used to describe this Dagenham-built Fordson. By 1935 when this shot was issued, production was well established at Dagenham. The air cleaner took its air from the steering column and was filled with water rather than oil. Hence this model is sometimes referred to as a 'Water washer Fordson'.** *Ian Allan Library*

Above: Industrial users were an important market for tractors in the 1930s. Ford did much to promote the idea that one Fordson industrial tractor could be used for several jobs by pulling different trailers. For this demonstration the trailer is the 'Eagle Hygienic Refuse Collector'. An ungoverned industrial running on petrol had a fair turn of speed and was little slower than any other commercial vehicle of the period — and much faster than horse-drawn equipment. The optional sweeping mudguards, cab and lighting system were rarely seen in service. *Ian Allan Library*

Above right: One of the first diesel conversions was offered by Ailsa Craig. Fitting one of its engines to a Fordson tractor meant cutting away part of the fuel tank. This conversion is an Industrial. Using a two-cylinder marine engine, it probably was a lot less flexible in use but would have lugged well. Newly introduced Dunlop wheels and tyres are fitted. The diesel conversion did not prove a commercial success. *Ian Allan Library*

Right: Not every 'vintage' tractor is as old as you might think. *Taw Valley Queen* was constructed by Mr K. Stenner in 1996. His aim was to display a three-cylinder Kelvin Marine engine he rescued and restored. Built in 1933, the engine powered a wooden coaster until 1970 when it was laid up and fell into disrepair. This unusual tractor highlights the fact that some rally exhibits may have more of a story behind them than you might suspect! *Author's Collection*

Above: **A proud moment for Aubrey Rees, who took over the Cirencester, Glos International franchise. To be able to take a consignment of five International 10-20s in the 1930s made good publicity. The sign board would have done duty on show stands as well. The tractors were dispatched fitted with road bands over the cleats. After the photographer had finished, they would be driven off and back to the works for checking over.** *Corinium Museum, Cirencester*

Left: **The original Ferguson prototype with hydraulic linkage. Built to demonstrate that the system worked, no PTO was fitted, nor was any form of towing hitch apart from the linkage.** *Agco*

Right: **The accepted explanation of how the forces generated by the plough hold the front of the tractor down, preventing rearing.** *Agco*

Even Fordsons were not immune to styling. Its effort was limited to changing the tractor colour from blue to a distinctive yellow-orange colour. One advantage of the colour change was that a farmer could spot his tractor and check it was at work at a greater distance. Unfortunately, it was later found that other, not so friendly, eyes could spot Fordsons from a greater distance, as we will see in the next chapter.

By the end of the 1930s it was accepted that a tractor was a sensible choice of power on a farm. Even so, only a minority of farms had tractors. The Ministry of Agriculture recorded about 50,000 tractors in England and Wales. Interestingly 3,000 older machines were reported as used for belt work only.

A tractor or stationary engine was seen as costing nothing when it was parked. While a horse could be used even when ground conditions were bad, a tractor could be used more intensively once conditions were right.

Even where farmers were using tractors they were not necessarily factory built. For example in Bridgwater,

Above: **A preserved example of the Ferguson Brown as it became known. The design was very different from other tractors on the market. Compact, the driver sat astride the tractor rather like a horseman. It was intended that all implements would attach to the tractor by the hydraulic linkage. The new design was received cautiously despite Ferguson's marketing flair.** *Author's Collection*

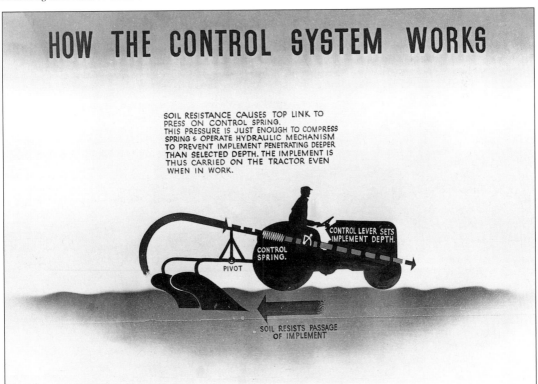

HOW THE CONTROL SYSTEM WORKS

SOIL RESISTANCE CAUSES TOP LINK TO
PRESS ON CONTROL SPRING.
THIS PRESSURE IS JUST ENOUGH TO COMPRESS
SPRING & OPERATE HYDRAULIC MECHANISM
TO PREVENT IMPLEMENT PENETRATING DEEPER
THAN SELECTED DEPTH. THE IMPLEMENT IS
THUS CARRIED ON THE TRACTOR EVEN
WHEN IN WORK.

CONTROL LEVER SETS
IMPLEMENT DEPTH.

CONTROL
SPRING.

PIVOT

SOIL RESISTS PASSAGE
OF IMPLEMENT

Left: **July 1939 saw the announcement of the first tractor to be sold under the 'Young' David Brown name. Having bought out Ferguson, David Brown (standing) was now an independent tractor manufacturer. The *Farmer & Stockbreeder* hailed it as a 'Clyde built model with steering light enough to be handled by a girl, which may be needed if war comes'. Even better, the company returned from the 1939 Royal Show at Windsor with orders for 3,000. (No doubt due to haste, the tyre tread is facing in the wrong direction.)** *Ian Allan Library*

Below left: **Patent restrictions meant that while a three-point linkage could be offered, implements needed a depth wheel. The simple cab was a short-lived innovation but the characteristic windshields were a feature until 1953. Electric starting and lights were optional extras but very welcome. The red livery chosen was based on that of David Brown's hunting jacket.** *Ian Allan Library*

Somerset, an agricultural engineer called Moss Heal offered conversion kits for motor cars. They involved attaching a complete car chassis to an old horse-drawn mower. The car's back axle was used to drive the mower wheels via a crude chain drive. Any local blacksmith could perform the union to produce quite a serviceable light tractor. It was capable of mowing, pulling a side-rake or tedder, or even a small trailer.

Other blacksmiths rigged up power drives direct to the mower knife as well as to the car wheels, using twin gearboxes. Jack Hatt, an Oxfordshire contractor, used to cut down big American Ford cars to produce his 'Hattford tractor'. Other farmers chopped the body-work off big cars to mount haysweeps on them.

These were all rough and ready conversions, but they met a need. Remember, many former arable farmers had let their farms revert to an all-grass regime, so powerful ploughing tractors were not needed.

Recognising the need to increase food production, the Minister of Agriculture introduced in 1939 a subsidy of £2 per acre for ploughing up grassland. Farmers began to consider their power requirements if they were going back to arable farming.

The declaration of war had a startling effect on the demand for machinery. Livestock farmers, faced with instructions to plough more land, needed tractors. Arable farmers, short of labour, needed more tractors. Enterprising young men were encouraged to start contract ploughing to help out neighbours.

The next six years were to have a dramatic effect on the use of tractors on British farms.

Top: **Pneumatic tyres might not be specified by every buyer, so steel wheels were available as an option.** *Ian Allan Library*

Above: **This first hydraulic lift was very quickly redesigned before production started.** *Ian Allan Library*

Below: **This simple drawbar was also quickly redesigned.** *Ian Allan Library*

Top: **Every so often somebody comes out with a radically new design for a tractor. S. E. Opperman announced and built the Mectaur. Details surviving are scant, mainly limited to these photographs plus an advertisement featuring the same power unit. Essentially it was a tractor with no front axle. Instead it plugged itself into a number of different implements, like the trailer. Presumably the steering wheel controlled the turntable, so that it acted as a pivot-steer outfit.** *Ian Allan Library*

Above: **Uncoupled it looks very unstable. For one man to lift the drawbar suggests that it would fall over backwards with a driver in the seat. In turn, that means the driver had to wheel the heavy power unit from implement to implement — no small job if an implement was uncoupled without forethought.** *Ian Allan Library*

Above: **With plough attached, the plough drawbar had to take the reaction from the tractor.** *Ian Allan Library*

Below: **Despite the unconventional design, it obviously worked after a fashion. It met an often-expressed desire for a tractor to replace a single horse. However, soon after the Mectaur was announced in 1939, Oppermans found itself engaged in war work overhauling aircraft landing gear.** *Ian Allan Library*

Above: Fitting a McLaren diesel on top of a Fowler ploughing engine cut running costs and gave it another lease of life without expensive boiler and firebox repairs. Forward visibility was poor! Nevertheless, this preserved example would have worked long and hard, especially during World War 2. A later modification was to replace the original starting donkey engine with a four-cylinder Morris Minor petrol engine. No cooling water is needed in this engine as the diesel normally starts before the engine overheats. One of a pair still at work cultivating ground in 1997 at the Fairford, Faringdon, Filkins & Burford Ploughing Society's 50th match. *Author's Collection*

Right: The two most influential men in tractor design together. Harry Ferguson (standing) demonstrating the principle of the Ferguson System with a clockwork model to Henry Ford. Ford acted promptly. *RASE*

Left: The Ford tractor with Ferguson System was the result. The American designers turned it into a stylish, well-engineered product fit for mass production. While Ford made them, Ferguson marketed them. The vast majority stayed in the USA but a trickle were imported to Britain where they were sold and serviced through Ford dealers. They demonstrated the abilities of the Ferguson System before production started at Coventry. *Author*

Above: Ford devoted a lot of thought to the most economical way of shipping tractors and spares. These skid packs saved the cost of the usual crates, although they were still needed for spare parts. The tractors in the foreground were destined for Calgary and Vancouver, Canada. As export tractors, the Fordson name appeared prominently on each mudguard. *Ian Allan Library*

Overleaf: Ford's Dagenham works became a familiar landmark to shipping up and down the Thames. Behind the prominent 'Ford' signs lay 66 acres of self-sufficient manufacturing plant. The cranes could load finished tractors straight into the holds of ships moored on the river side of the 600yd jetty. Other ships would be unloading bulk coal, ore or limestone. You can see why the RAF felt bright orange tractors would make an inviting target. *Ian Allan Library*

4. WARTIME DEMANDS, 1939-45

The outbreak of war presented a challenge for agriculture. Farmers had always accepted the risks of investing time and money in growing excellent crops. What was beyond their control was to be told, once the crop was harvested, that the 'market price' was so low that it was not worth enough to be profitable, owing to cheap imports. Belatedly, the country acknowledged that their entire production and more was urgently needed.

Once the shortages of World War 1 had been overcome, successive Governments had reverted to a short-term policy of encouraging cheap imports of food from all parts of the world to hold down the cost of living. What the Government had overlooked was the time lag between preparing the ground to receive a crop and food being ready for use by hungry consumers.

For example, war was declared on 3 September 1939. Suppose a patriotic farmer ploughed a grassland field the next day, cultivated the soil and planted winter wheat. Assuming it survived attack from the wireworm

Below: The Allis Chalmers U was a well-proven American tractor. This was the first model to adopt pneumatic tyres. Old time tractor drivers still recall its sense of smooth, effortless power, both pulling implements and on the belt pulley. With a top speed of 10mph in fourth gear, the first owner of this example must have been delighted when it arrived in Gloucestershire in 1942. *Author*

Right: The Caterpillar D2 was launched as a medium agricultural crawler. Long after being classed as obsolete, many were kept in reserve for very wet conditions. Starting was by a petrol donkey engine. This rotated and warmed the main engine before starting, reducing wear. *Author's Collection*

Below right: The Fowler Gyrotiller was originally designed to cultivate ground for growing sugar cane. Tracks ensured it could travel over rough ground but most of the engine power was fed to driving the two large rotors. Working at a depth of up to 2ft/600mm, they could cut through roots and other obstructions, leaving a strip of cultivated soil behind. It was difficult to find profitable work in Britain for them until the need for land reclamation during World War 2. At last these machines found a use — the irony was that Fowlers were not in a position to build any more. *Ray Bird*

The Ford works at Dagenham was the main source of tractors during World War 2. The 150,000th tractor built is typical of the wartime specification, with steel wheels and narrowed wings to save steel. In 1943 the factory built 26,990 tractors. By 10 November it had produced 100,000 tractors since war broke out. That was roughly twice the population of tractors in Britain at the start of the war. The original of this photograph is marked 'Passed by Photographic Censor M.O.I. March 30, 1943.'
Ian Allan Library

in the turf, it would be fit to harvest in August 1940. Cutting with a binder meant that it would be carted and stacked in the sheaf, so before the wheat could be used it had to be threshed. This might not be possible until March 1941. Then the grain had to be transported off the farm and milled before the flour was available to mix with imported grain for breadmaking in, say, May 1941.

This left the prowling submarines a whole 20 months to attack shipping to offset this increase in cropping. Yet to replace the cargo of just one merchant ship sunk bringing imported wheat would need 500 farmers to decide to grow an extra 10 acres each of wheat.

One reason the Government was caught out so badly was that expenditure on re-armament and civil prepa-

rations had been deferred. Amazingly, forward planning assumed there would be at least 10 years' warning of any impending war.

This extraordinary suggestion was first made in 1919 and persisted until the late 1930s. It was originally laid down as an assumption for service planning. Only by implication was it applied to agriculture. An important attraction of this assumption was savings in the national budget.

Some emergency planning had been carried out. As in World War 1, the Minister of Agriculture acted through County War Agricultural Executive Committees. These were known universally as 'War Ags' and were normally made up of successful farmers and landowners within the county, together with representatives of the County Council and workers' unions.

Much of their work was done by District Committees. Effectively each farmer was directed as to what crops to grow and what livestock to keep. This was done by issuing cropping orders which gave specific instructions about how a field was to be cultivated and sown.

Many farmers who had been running an all-grass system (and large numbers of farms had resorted to this in the 1920s) found themselves instructed to plough up grassland and grow crops. Part of the reasoning was to try to concentrate on producing bulky, filling crops rather than, say, high quality beef.

To be instructed to grow cereals was daunting enough for a livestock farmer; many were instructed to grow potatoes. This crop had the potential to produce plenty of bulk. In nutritional terms it produced more starch per acre than wheat. In crude terms, plenty of spuds stopped the population feeling hungry.

It was one thing to be told to grow potatoes, but how to do it? Many farmers had no suitable arable implements. Second-hand implements commanded high prices from farmers eager to get on with the job. There were nowhere near enough horses to cope with demand

and few farmers were willing to sell. With petrol rationing looming, town users were looking to replace motor vans with horses as well.

Tractors were the answer: from the Ford plant at Dagenham, the first of the David Browns from Huddersfield, Marshalls from Gainsborough, Fowler crawlers from Leeds and small crawlers from Ransomes at Ipswich.

Only Dagenham was in a position to step up production, which it did to great effect. None of the other makers was permitted to make a big increase in output.

Imports were the only answer. Lanz tractors had proved sturdy and reliable, but although they were selling right up to the declaration of war, no more could be expected from that source. Allis Chalmers, Case, Caterpillar, John Deere, International, Massey Harris, Minneapolis Moline and Oliver were all represented on the British market but sales had been slow.

Now they faced a tremendous demand. Soon 'permits to acquire' were needed to purchase a new tractor.

Left and below: **To help train new drivers, Fordson supplied a number of sectioned instructional tractors. Cutaways meant a trainee could peer right into the insides of the tractor. Even for drivers who were not expected to undertake repairs, it was a great confidence booster. For example, they could see for themselves how the heat of the exhaust manifold was used to vaporise the fuel before it was sucked into the engine.** *Both: Author*

These were administered by the Machinery Officers of the War Ags.

Their aim was to direct available tractors to the farms where they could do the most useful work. Where possible, these permits took account of the local servicing arrangements and the crops being grown. Even with imports, over 75% of tractors were still home-built Fordsons. The bigger American tractors went to replace traction engines on threshing drums or to bigger farms.

Occasionally surprises turned up. Two farmers have recounted getting crated John Deeres delivered. When unpacked and assembled, one arable farm found itself with an orchard model, while the other received a crawler when it was expecting a row crop tractor.

Many American tractors came through the US Lend Lease Act which enabled goods to be shipped without awaiting payment. This scheme was used to cover the shipment of military material as well, although under the terms of the Act it was thought that bulldozers, for instance, could not be used for certain military construction jobs. As a result David Brown was instructed to build some crawlers which it did, fitting Dorman engines.

Farmers who did place orders for American-built tractors found that delivery promises were not always reliable. With the outbreak of war, merchant shipping became a target for German submarines. Out in mid-Atlantic they could operate out of range of escorting aircraft.

The first convoys took dreadful losses. The mental strain on the crews must have been appalling. Often the first they would know of a torpedo attack would be a shattering explosion. One can only admire the bravery of the merchant seamen who returned to such frightening conditions for voyage after voyage.

Of course, farmers were not aware of the full picture at the time. Perhaps through friends or relatives they would hear of a particular ship being lost. Maybe they even harboured the unworthy thought that their promised tractor had been diverted elsewhere.

Many tractor fuel tanks carried the slogan 'We won't waste it Sailor' to encourage fuel economy. Few drivers

Above left and above: **Here is an interesting mystery.** Although quite clearly badged as a diesel, this International McCormick WD6 appears to be a spark ignition tractor. Before jumping to any conclusions, have a look at the other side of the engine. As you would expect with a diesel, you find an injector pump. This is a preserved example of one of the early petrol-start diesels produced by International. No starter motor was needed, as the engine could be hand-started as a petrol engine. Once warm, the fuel systems were changed over and it ran as a diesel. While it sounds complicated, it proved a very effective starting system at a time when diesels were still unusual on farms. When this tractor first arrived in Worcestershire in 1941, it must have represented a very welcome power boost. *Both: Author*

Above right and right: **The David Brown Thresherman was** reworked in 1946 from airfield towing tractors. Stylish mudguards covered all four wheels. These were made from heavy plate and provided extra ballast. More pig iron weights could be attached underneath to increase the all-up weight. Braking was still only on the back wheels. From new this had been fitted with a winch. The conversion gained the adjustable hitch, together with a front-mounted belt pulley. This offered a useful unit to meet the threshing contractors' specialised needs. The chap on the left is tackling what is normally the dustiest job on a threshing drum: raking out the cavings. The unguarded belt was accepted practice but putting the scales right underneath was rather dangerous for the chap bagging off. No doubt the photograph was carefully posed. *Both: Ian Allan Library*

fully appreciated the grim reality behind the slogan.

For security reasons shipping losses could not be made generally known. The Chairmen of the War Ags were briefed on the vital importance of growing all that was possible to save shipping space which was too precious to transport food that could be grown in Britain. They were expected to return to their counties and enthuse their committees, staff and farmers to increase output.

War Ags did much more than just chase local farmers. Their machinery officers operated equipment hire schemes so that suitable farmers and contractors could hire equipment on favourable terms.

Probably their most spectacular activities were their land reclamation ventures. Earlier in the 1930s Fowlers had built a number of powered rotary digging machines mounted on its crawler tractors. Intended for cultivating sugar cane fields after harvest, they were a powerful replacement for steam ploughing sets. A number of these Gyrotillers remained in Britain, mainly operated by steam ploughing contractors. Although manufacture had ceased, at last Gyrotillers found a task for which they were ideally suited. The rotating blades were ideal for stirring up the soil and loosening the roots of scrub. The land was left rather hollow and puffy, but at least it was in a state that other implements could cope with.

Steam ploughing engines came back into favour in some areas. As well as for heavy ploughing and cultivating, they proved ideal for dragging out trees bodily to be burned.

Draglines were used to restore or replace old drainage systems and overgrown fields were transformed to productive use. Mountainsides were cleared to make fields at high altitudes. Neglected marshes were drained and cultivated. Golf courses and parks were ploughed up for agriculture. Commons and other rough grazing were reclaimed.

The War Ag tractor fleets grew rapidly. For example, by the end of the war Essex WAEC had over 500 tractors, mainly Fordsons. Montgomeryshire had a fleet of International crawlers used to reclaim hillsides for growing potatoes on land previously used for sheep. The height above sea level was such that aphids were not a problem, so they were able to specialise in growing seed potatoes.

As fast as the War Ags were regaining land, other land was being lost for airfields and other military requirements. The urgent need would have resulted in a loss of land had it not been for the programme of reclamation. These extra acres needed tractors.

When selecting land for airfields, the Air Ministry preferred to take fertile farms rather than neglected land. Their reasoning was that these would grow the best crop of grass. This would knit together to form well-matted turf, needed to support aircraft landing and taking off as concrete runways did not become common until later on in the war.

Ford at Dagenham had responded marvellously to the demand for tractors. In mid-1943 the Minister of Agriculture visited the factory to thank the workers for their efforts. According to the Ministry of Information's censored press statement, Mr R. S. Hudson told them, 'We started war with 50,000 tractors. By the start of 1943 we had 120,000 tractors. Over 80% of these are Fordsons.'

That implies 70,000 tractors put into service in just over three years, with about 56,000 built at Dagenham. No wonder the pace of change was like a whirlwind on farms. It took nearly 40 years to get 50,000 tractors into service. In the next three years Ford more than doubled the tractor population *on their own*. On top of that another 14,000 American tractors were at work

More immediately, the flow of tractors meant that skilled drivers were needed. Some were existing farm workers retrained, others were volunteers; often a schoolboy would be the quickest at grasping this new technology. Agricultural colleges were running courses to train their students as drivers. Ford had a training school at Boreham for older boys, which offered a one-year course. Their students were in turn able to pass on instruction when they started work.

Oxford University was an early pioneer of research in agricultural engineering. This led to the formation of the National Institute of Agricultural Engineering. Once transferred to Askham Bryan in Yorkshire, it quickly identified the need to improve the tractor driving skills of operators.

To make this possible it produced a series of silent films of various combinations of tractors and implements being operated correctly. These had the great advantage that they could be shown on the 16mm film projectors that were just becoming available. If electricity was available in a village hall, an instructor could

Left and below: **Nearly 60 years ago some-body else looked thoughtfully at this Morris van and saw a potential tractor. With chains on the back wheels and plenty of ballast, it would probably do the work of a good horse, especially in dry weather. Ploughing would be out of the question, but for haymaking or harvest it would be a great help. Many of these conversions were carried out by local blacksmiths, especially during the war when petrol rationing meant potential tractors could be bought cheaply. Certainly they were crude but being on pneumatic tyres they were probably faster than a tractor on steel wheels. Exhibited at Fairford Steam Rally in 1997, this van had been restored back from the tractor conversion shown.** *Both: Author*

arrange to have the film shown, allowing novice tractor drivers to become familiar with procedure even before the tractor was delivered.

Many skilled tractor drivers were called up or volunteered for military service, even though they were in a 'reserved occupation'. Willing volunteers were pressed into service. As a result, one Wiltshire farmer selling his old Fordson many years later was able to boast his tractor had only two regular drivers — himself and a duchess!

This was no time though for major innovations in tractor design. Most of the tractors built or imported were well-proven designs. There were, however, lots of minor changes in order to cope with shortages. Most tractors were supplied on steel wheels unless there was an overpowering need for pneumatic tyres. Mudguards on Fordsons got smaller to save steel. Lengthening the drop arm made the steering easier for female drivers. German-made Bosch magnetos were replaced by a Lucas equivalent. Even the American makers were affected by shortages of strategic materials like rubber.

For the first time since 1921 farmers felt needed. They felt justified in investing in up-to-date machinery. The demand even resulted in the arrival of a few early diesels among the crawlers and wheeled tractors from the USA.

Massey Harris tractors used a variety of bought-in truck engines for powering its various models. Its four-wheel drive design in the mid-1930s had been very advanced but a commercial failure. Now its designers were concentrating on a self-propelled combine rather than tractor improvements.

Tractors solved many problems for the Royal Air Force. Bombs were transported from stockpiles to aircraft using low, four-wheeled trolleys pulled in trains behind Fordson tractors. These were basic agricultural types; indeed some were even commandeered locally.

Other batches were supplied with high-speed final drives for faster travel. Running on straight petrol (often aviation spirit), they had a surprising turn of speed.

Moving a loaded bomber over soft ground was rather more of a challenge. To meet this task some Fordsons were converted to crawler tractors and fitted with a powerful winch. This work was carried out by Roadless Traction at Hounslow. To support the front-mounted winch, many of the Fordsons retained their front axle which was remounted in front of the winch. This conversion resulted in an outfit that had the power and control to move aircraft over difficult ground conditions.

David Brown was directed to specialise in aircraft towing tractors. These came with a rear-mounted winch and anchors. For smoother towing some were fitted with a Brockhouse torque converter which replaced the clutch and gave a very gentle take up of drive.

It may seem strange to divert tractors to the RAF when they were so urgently needed on farms, but using tractors to move aircraft and bombs saved the wear and tear caused by taxying aircraft on the ground. It also meant that planes could be moved without needing a flight crew at the controls.

Tractor enthusiasts are always attracted by scrapyards where old tractors accumulate. For years this yard in Norfolk was one such magnet. An extra bonus was that it was right alongside an excellent transport cafe. In 1978 the tractors in this yard illustrated the mixture of American wartime imports that came to the aid of Norfolk agriculture. *Author's Collection*

When many of these tractors were sold off after the war they were eagerly snapped up. Most of the released Fordsons were converted to paraffin operation. Contractors especially welcomed examples with faster gearing to give quicker travel between jobs. The Roadless crawlers were appreciated for their extra traction. On farm work the winch was sometimes removed and replaced by ballast. Other users retained the winch, which proved very useful when other tractors got stuck.

Postwar, some of the David Browns were modified with a front-mounted belt pulley to make specialist threshing tractors. Many of them retained the additional pig iron ballast stowed underneath the chassis. This extra weight meant the tractor weighed nearly as much as the threshing drum, which improved control when towing. Not surprisingly, other winch tractors found a second career as timber tractors.

Tractor makers were also manufacturing parts for military use. David Brown made output gears for aircraft engines; Ford built Rolls-Royce Merlin aircraft engines, Bren gun carriers and lorries; Morris rebuilt crashed aircraft; Marshall built midget submarines; Fowler made tank components.

One of the great pleasures of today's vintage rallies is meeting some of the older visitors who were tractor drivers in the 1940s. If you are prepared to listen, it is still possible to hear their first-hand accounts of working with tractors in wartime.

The schoolboy son of a tractor driver was one of them. He recalled that a horse was often used to help their Ford Ferguson both downhill and uphill with heavier loads. Only one horse could be used for braking as there was only one suitable set of harness with a breech strap on the farm. He still recalls the excitement when a new Case LA arrived and he was allowed to drive it. 'I felt like a million dollars with the new tractor.' Although he could crank up the tractor to start it, elation turned to bitter tears as the steering on cultivated ground proved too heavy for his schoolboy strength. To his chagrin he was back to driving the Ford Ferguson. Farms were very pushed for labour and a useful schoolboy like him would have been highly prized. (Writer A. G. Street's father reckoned that one boy was nearly as useful as a man but two boys together were useless.)

On that farm as with many, much help came from 'Land Girls'. No Women's Land Army recruits had

Massey Harris tractors were more of an unknown quantity during the war. Supply difficulties meant several different bought-in lorry engines were used and many were later replaced with Perkins diesels. Despite this, the tractor shown was over 30 years old and was still on its original engine in 1975. It is seen being used to transport a slightly older (and slower) Fordson to a ploughing match. When it was built, Massey Harris designers were concentrating on the self-propelled combine which proved a real world-beater.
Author's Collection

more than three months' experience of farm work; most had none. Once enlisted, they were trained as dairy workers, general farm workers, rat catchers or tractor drivers. When trained, they could be posted to any part of the country. Many farmers were dubious about the contribution they could make, but they quickly established a good reputation. Tractor driving was one of the less popular options. It is not surprising when you recall an early press report from one training college. 'Miss…broke her wrist trying to start a tractor. When she returned from sick leave she decided to train as a dairy maid instead.'

The Women's Timber Corps, the 'Lumberjills', specialised in forestry work.

Even less well known was that as in World War 1 some serving soldiers were posted to a corps of tractor drivers. Privates were ordinary tractor drivers; Corporal tractor drivers acted as supervisors, but still drove tractors. Other NCOs were not allowed to drive.

Many military units 'lent a hand on the land' for short periods as a break from training. Many farm workers were in the Home Guard, so their 'spare time' was spent guarding their home village against enemy attack.

From Berkshire comes this alarming wartime tale of getting the threshing done. A farmer at Lambourn still used a Burrell compound steam engine. The regular driver's son told me his recollections. As a young schoolboy he would be left stoking, controlling the engine and minding the gauges, while father sacked off grain from the threshing drum. You might think this a very irresponsible way to operate but remember we are considering wartime emergency conditions. Any normally inquisitive son would have watched Dad working from an early age. Unknowingly, son would have learned a lot about the management of a steamer. While bagging off the grain, Dad was doubtless listening to the engine. If he heard anything amiss, he could be on the man-stand in a couple of seconds. Many steam engine drivers tell me that a bellow from Dad when they were six

years old has stopped them doing something stupid many years later.

Wartime conditions ensured another lease of life for steamers before retirement. Steamers need major and expensive repairs, but at infrequent intervals. These are usually the result of failing a boiler inspection by the insurance company's engineer.

A farmer acquiring a second-hand steam engine for temporary use hoped it could survive for two or three inspections without needing much work. If so, steam could make a worthwhile contribution to wartime power needs. A curiously large number of engines were finally condemned in 1945 as needing major repairs. Insurance engineers may have slightly relaxed their standards during the emergency.

You might think that tractor driving in wartime would be much the same as in peacetime. Far from it. Tractors were in short supply and much land was being ploughed for the first time in living memory. Many farms that had reverted to grass had no cultivation implements, let alone a tractor.

Thus it was quickly realised that the only way to get the work done was to work long hours. No longer could a farmer who was well equipped with tractors plan to finish his ploughing in good time. If work was finished on his farm, he could be directed to assist less well-equipped neighbours. In fact, direction was rarely needed as there was a strong sense of common purpose.

Those with steel wheels would be left overnight in the field, covered with a sheet. At first light the driver would refuel, check round the tractor before starting another long day ploughing. Meals were often no more than sandwiches eaten as work continued. Ploughing often carried on after dark. This would be helped by marking out the field and ploughing the first few furrows of each bout in daylight.

As darkness fell, ploughing could be continued by dropping the front wheel of the tractor into the trench left by the previous furrow. Using this as a guide a few

Above: **John Deere row crop tractors like this wartime Model A were directed mainly to potato growers. With their unusual 'pop pop' exhaust note, they were very distinctive. No starting handle was supplied and starting was by grasping the flywheel and rotating it. The reputation left by wartime imports helped John Deere re-establish itself when it resumed marketing in Britain.** *Author's Collection*

Right: **One of the lesser known outfits of World War 2 was the Women's Timber Corps. An offshoot of the Women's Land Army, they specialised in forestry work. Here they are loading pit props they had previously felled and cut to length near Corfe Castle. This posed photograph makes it look a pleasant job. Many of the jobs undertaken by the 'Lumberjills', as they were known, were under far less pleasant conditions. This Fordson would probably have been built in 1939, hence the pneumatic tyres. Forestry work can be hard on tyres. With wartime shortages, it was vital the driver did not damage a tyre on a protruding tree stump.** *IAL*

Above: **The Oliver 80 was another wartime import. Smooth running, well-engineered tractors, they were well thought of by farmers lucky enough to get an example. The Bamford Mower was a more robust version of its horse-drawn design. This restored outfit was taking part in a working demonstration in Wiltshire in 1990, which brought back many memories.** *Author's Collection*

Right: **This 1940 Fendt was imported and restored by Bill Bennett (standing). He found it in a scrapyard within 400yd of the Fendt works in Germany. A 16hp Deutz engine drove through a three-speed gearbox to a rear axle fitted with a differential lock. Despite its compact size, it proved capable of pulling a two-furrow plough with ease. Its first outing restored was to the 1976 Highland Show. To Fendt's great surprise, the restored tractor aroused great interest whenever exhibited. This was one small part of Bill's efforts to promote this previously unknown make.** *Author's Collection*

more rounds could be completed before work had to stop for the day. Blackout regulations strictly limited the amount of light that could be displayed by a tractor. Few tractors had lights, but even torches and paraffin pressure lanterns were banned at first.

Petrol was strictly rationed, so starting a paraffin tractor had to be planned. The engine needed to be warmed up quickly so that it could be changed from petrol to paraffin.

War brought more immediate hazards for some drivers. In 1940 out in the fields of Kent or Sussex it became vital to be aware of what was going on overhead. With the Battle of Britain in progress, dogfights were frequent. Spent ammunition would be falling to the ground as well as damaged aircraft. One driver was startled to have the tail wheel of a Spitfire fall from the sky and land just between his Fordson and the binder he was towing.

Sometimes the hazard was not from enemy attack. With aerodromes scattered around the country, there was plenty of unused grass between the runways. Local farmers were permitted to mow these patches. This pro-

One early customer for a Ford Ferguson was Frank Perkins. He fitted it with a prototype of the P3 engine he proposed to build. This was the smallest member of the P family. Either as conversions or original equipment, they powered many different makes of tractor. It could be said that here was also the prototype of the Fordson Dexta, 23 years before it was launched! *Ian Allan Library*

vided welcome extra winter feed when made into hay. It also made a useful area to disperse stores around the airfield as a protection against enemy attack. Mowing involved cutting around these dumps.

Picture the scene: the keen, young tractor driver with his steel-wheeled Fordson is cutting as close as possible to the dumps. As he approaches one dump the front of the tractor starts to jolt. Realising he must have driven over something, he declutches. Looking down, he finds to his horror that he has driven over a layer of bombs that have been concealed in long grass! He realises that alongside are more bombs neatly stacked! What to do next? Blind instinct takes over. Reasoning the RAF will not be very pleased if he damages any of their bombs, he drops the tractor into reverse and backs off. Once again the steel front wheels jolt over the bombs! From the fact that he was telling the story, he got away with it — but what a frightening moment.

Despite all the extra problems, tractor drivers coped manfully, ensuring that Britain did not starve. This was greatly helped by the Allies getting on top of the submarine menace in the North Atlantic.

The Ford Dagenham factory had produced 137,000 tractors by the end of the war. This had been achieved despite 200 bombs being dropped on the factory, as well as the bombing attacks suffered on their homes by Ford workers. With no export sales, it is hardly surprising that on most farms their first tractor at least was a Fordson. In many cases the farm would still retain some horses, but the Fordson would be there to do the heavy work.

Early in 1945 the shape of the Fordson changed with the introduction of what became the Fordson Major. The Ministry of Agriculture requirement to Ford was that its new tractor should:
- be capable of pulling three furrows on any kind of land;
- offer lower fuel consumption;
- offer greater horsepower;
- require no phosphor bronze in the axle.

Above: **When Ford celebrated its 75th anniversary in 1978, it featured a Fordson N as part of the display. This was fitting because during World War 2, 80% of tractors on British farms were Fordsons of various ages. Mind you, the tractor displayed probably left Dagenham on steel wheels.** *Author's Collection*

Right: **Despite having the same engine, the (E27N) Fordson Major looked much bigger than a Fordson N. The main difference was the revised transmission and the bigger rear wheels. At the front the axle was mounted lower to lift the engine. These changes left room for underslung implements for row crop work. Despite being a stopgap model, the Major sold strongly until replaced in 1952.** *Author's Collection*

The Ministry of Supply stipulated this had to be achieved with no new tooling for the engine and the absolute minimum of modifications to the transmission.

Within these tight constraints the Fordson Major was an effective design. The gearbox remained almost unchanged but the final drive was through a crown wheel and pinion and reduction gears.

Together with bigger diameter wheels, this transformed the look of the tractor. The extra clearance underneath left room for mid-mounted equipment. Mounting pads were machined to take attachments. Dished wheels could

be mounted in different ways to alter wheel spacings for row crop work, for which an adjustable front axle could also be specified. As they became available, provision was made so that the Major could be built with hydraulic lift and/or PTO.

This was not the tractor Ford wanted to make but it made an effective stopgap model and nearly a quarter of a million were to be built over the next seven years. Despite the good service Dagenham had given the country, it would shortly find itself up against strong competition.

With victory and peace you might have thought the demand for food would have diminished. Far from it. In the next few years, demands on both farmers and tractor manufacturers were to increase.

5. POSTWAR RECOVERY, 1945-52

The end of World War 2 meant few immediate changes for agriculture. Demand for food was still strong, with food shortages all over mainland Europe. The high cost of modern warfare had left the country in a serious financial state. As a trading nation much of Britain's income had come from exports of manufactured goods. While Britain was not in a position to supply, many former customers had gone elsewhere, or had been unable to buy at all. Factories were short of skilled men and often were manufacturing products no longer required. Some engineering companies decided agriculture was a good market to aim for.

Government controls reduced imports that had to be paid for in dollars. Fewer American tractors were allowed in. Several American makers were 'persuaded' to start assembly or manufacture in Britain.

Dollar shortages meant that even the peacetime Fordson Major still had to retain the old familiar power unit, although from 1948 some Fordson Majors were supplied from new, fitted with Perkins P6 diesel engines.

For Harry Ferguson the dollar shortages represented both an opportunity and a problem. Opportunity because the Government was receptive to his ideas of introducing a new British tractor factory; problem because dollars would be needed to import engines and tooling to get production under way.

Standard Motors of Coventry had expanded during the war. With peace, its massive factory would need work to keep it profitably employed. To meet this need Standard experimented in 1945 with a versatile four-wheel drive utility for farmers. On smaller and fatter tyres than the Land Rover, it too was planned as a combination of light tractor and private car. Although little

The Fordson Major offered the option of a hydraulic system. As here, it could be used to power a hydraulic loader. Although that has been removed, the PTO is in use driving this Walley Gang Mo grass harvester with an unguarded shaft. Clippings from trailing gang mowers are collected on elevators and deposited in the trailer behind. While the grass was kept short and tidy, the harvested material was ideal for grass drying.
National Motor Museum, Beaulieu

Top: Having only supplied a few agricultural tractors in the previous five years, David Brown explored various possible outlets for their potential production. For 1946 it was able to make some improvements to its tractor. The kerosine agricultural version was the VAK/1A. This is the much less common petrol-engined industrial version with down-swept exhaust, the VIG/1A. *Ian Allan Library*

Above: Building on its experience of airfield towing tractors, David Brown was well placed for the heavy industrial market. Sales were not large, as many jobs which might have called for industrial tractors were now done by lorries or even ex-Government tractors. *Ian Allan Library*

Above: **Although designed to work with linkage-mounted implements, a Ferguson could cope with trailed implements such as a binder. The light and positive controls made it ideal for women drivers. The tyre treads show this was an early example; surprisingly, the rear tyres have been mounted with the tread in the wrong direction.** *Agco*

Left: **With Henry Ford dead, Harry Ferguson grabbed the headlines in Detroit with his court case against the Ford Company. Posed photographs like this were an important part of his sustained publicity campaign against Ford. In the end he was able to claim victory.** *Agco*

has since been heard of this prototype, it was field tested by the *Farmer & Stockbreeder* magazine in 1945.

Instead Harry Ferguson persuaded Standard Motors to build Ferguson tractors for him at Banner Lane, Coventry. Completed tractors would be sold to Ferguson, at the factory gate at a negotiated price. Effectively Standard carried all the risk.

What emerged was the Ferguson TE 20, an overhead-valve engined four-speed development of the Ford Ferguson. Here was a light and handy tractor capable of doing a surprising amount of work. Imported Continental engines were fitted until Standard developed their 2-litre engine, which could also be fitted to the Vanguard car. Many of the early tractors were petrol only. It was felt that with electric starting they would be stopped rather than left idling. TVO and lamp oil versions followed. Reluctantly, a diesel version was later added, based on the same engine, although Ferguson was doubtful whether it was needed.

Strong demand for Ferguson tractors ensured the deal worked out well for both parties. Farmers had been sceptical about the Ferguson Brown but the war had made them much more tractor-minded. The few Ford Fergusons had performed remarkable feats and earned a good reputation. Harry Ferguson had honed his selling skills in the American market and Ferguson tractors sold well all over the world. When production ended in 1956, over half a million tractors had rolled off the assembly line at Banner Lane.

Buying the first tractor for a farm has always been only the start of spending money. Without implements to pull and drive, a tractor can do little useful work.

Ferguson publicity was directed to persuading farmers that they needed both a light tractor *and* its associated implements. The two-furrow plough was usually the first implement chosen. While the Ferguson was light enough to be matched to horse-drawn implements, there would be pressure to get them replaced with the appropriate mounted implement 'to get the best from the Ferguson System'.

This really paid off when the next tractor was required. The only tractor that all the implements would easily fit was another Ferguson! Of course, other makers soon introduced models that could take most implements. However, a good Ferguson salesman would make farmers doubt the wisdom of changing make. They were good because they were well trained. Most had been on one or more courses at the Ferguson Training School at Stoneleigh Abbey. Ferguson insisted on the highest standards in appearance and technical knowledge from any representative.

Across the Atlantic a big problem arose following the death of Henry Ford. The new management at Ford Motor Co decided they would no longer supply Ferguson with tractors to sell. Deprived of supply, many Ferguson dealers switched allegiance to Ford's new marketing organisation, Dearborn Tractor Company.

This lost Ferguson many good dealers. To supply the remainder, Ferguson managed to start tractor production in the United States but obviously he was badly hit financially. A number of British-built tractors were shipped across as a stopgap. To American enthusiasts these British-built Fergusons are known as 'Harrys'.

This led to a protracted legal case in which Ferguson sued Ford under 'Anti Trust' legislation. Winning the case gained him heavy damages from Ford, and certain features still under patent had to be removed from future Ford tractors. Fergusons were being built on both sides of the Atlantic but with detail differences. The Ford tractor, their most direct competitor in the USA, had clearly evolved from the Ford Ferguson design. You cannot help admiring an inventor who could cope with so many problems while bringing his idea to the market. His strength was a strong belief in the worth to farmers of what he was doing. He managed to surround himself with associates that could make what he visualised.

Ferguson had established himself as a motor engineer in Belfast before World War 1, after making a name for himself both in motor racing and as the first Irishman to

Left: **The Ferguson 20 was seen in some unexpected places. Harry Ferguson drives one into the Savoy Hotel to enliven a dealers' meeting. There was just time for the hotel to cover the carpet!** *Agco*

Below: **In Antarctica Sir Edmund Hillary's team unloads stores with Fergusons, in preparation for their expedition to the South Pole. Apart from the non-standard tracks and windscreen, they are normal production tractors but with the maximum engine speed increased to 3,000rpm.** *Agco*

With the hydraulic linkage part of the Ferguson System, designers took advantage of this to simplify new implements. This angle blade was suitable for snow clearance and light levelling. The rear wheels are fitted with girdles. These wrapped round the tyre. When the tractor was pulling, they rotated slightly to dig into the soil for extra grip. They were at their most effective when the tractor tyres were getting worn. The diesel engine proved very successful and popular once it was offered as an option. *Ian Allan Library*

fly an aircraft (which he also built). Without these resources he would not have been able to finance the development work that produced the three-point linkage and the Ferguson system.

The Ford action must have been particularly difficult for him personally, as he and old Henry Ford had so much in common. Ford's family came from Ireland; both detested the drudgery of farm labour and both had a strong belief in mechanising this work. Ford had just got interested in aviation when they first met. Both had made their names by racing fast cars. Both had an enormous impact on the 20th century. Both had a habit of publishing their thoughts on how they could relieve world poverty. Maybe their relationship was nearer father and son rather than business associates? Certainly both had a tremendous impact on agriculture.

The Agriculture Act of 1947 laid the foundation for sustained demand for output from Britain's farms. Guaranteed prices were laid down. Critics have claimed these were subsidies but it ensured consumers got their supply of cheap and wholesome food.

Although tractors were still on allocation, farmers were keen to invest in them. Despite the increase in available horsepower, more workers were being engaged. This was probably due to the backlog of jobs that had built up during the war. It also allowed people a chance to work at a slightly slower tempo than during the wartime emergency. The repatriation of German and Italian prisoners of war who had stayed on, helping on farms, was mostly completed by 1948. Some did stay on, as did many 'displaced persons', mostly ex-servicemen who originated from countries overrun by the Russians.

This prompted a sales claim for the new Field Marshall that would jar a modern reader. Marshall used to claim its tractors were 'particularly suitable to be driven by displaced persons'. Although a pretty tasteless remark, it is certainly true that 'Johnny the Pole', who was a mechanic at Wilders of Reading, was the company's expert on Marshall repairs and servicing. Johnny was a real Marshall enthusiast and proved how the presence of a good mechanic often had more influence than a salesman on a farmer's buying decisions.

The year 1948 saw the formation of the National Agricultural Advisory Service. Financed by the Ministry of Agriculture, its job was to offer advice and assistance to farmers to increase output. This included providing advice on mechanisation. NAAS took over many of the functions of local authority advisers and the technical officers of the War Ags.

It was often at a NAAS demonstration that a farmer gained ideas for his next step forward. To prevent claims of bias, some of the demonstrations that were organised had to feature some fairly unpromising approaches to solving a problem. Luckily, the advisers could rely on the common sense of most of their farmers not to be taken in.

Many surplus military vehicles were released for sale. Jeeps, gun tractors and 15cwt personnel carriers in particular provided extra tractor power on many farms.

Above: The use of machinery was an important part of an agricultural college education. Students are being instructed on the diesel engined Ferguson TEF. The instructor is drawing their attention to the Ki-Gass cold starting aid. Its correct use was to inject additional volatile starting fluid into the manifold to aid cold starting. Unofficially it could be used as a temporary boost to performance. While harmful to the engine, there is no telling what students got up to when out of sight of an instructor! *Royal Agricultural College*

Right: While many Fergusons have been scrapped, others still linger on, used for odd jobs. Despite its battered and neglected appearance, this Fergie was still doing a useful job carting the winter firewood. With luck, by now it will have been acquired by an enthusiast. Many of the immaculate Fergusons to be seen at vintage rallies were in a far worse condition when rescued. *Ray Bird*

Rather than ploughing and cultivating, they were used mainly for transport and haulage work. In the same way, four-wheel drive lorries carried lime spreader bodies. These replaced tractor-drawn spreaders for contractors, where their high road speed and limited weather protection for the driver was welcome. Other ex-military vehicles pressed into service were Muir Hill Dumpers mounted on Fordson tractors. These had good traction and were used as internal farm transport.

In a classic 'swords into ploughshares' move, a few tanks were used as heavy duty crawler tractors. The first trial using a tank as an agricultural tractor had been carried out during the war to see if any use could be found for the Covenantor. Crawfords of Frithville, Lincs, engineers and contractors, have preserved the Sherman tank they once used. Noisy and powerful it certainly was. The problem of moving it from job to job soon made the idea impractical, once traffic regulations became more important than food production.

With large quantities of uniforms released by the military, many tractor drivers discovered that battledress blouse and trousers, greatcoat and beret made a practical working outfit. Haversacks proved ideal for the lunchtime sandwiches and bottle of cold tea.

Many countrymen were only too happy to put military service behind them in favour of work on the farm. Others invested their gratuities in a farm or an agricultural engineering business. Skills learned in military service provided a foundation for a garage or jobbing agricultural engineers.

In 1947 the Ground Nut Scheme was conceived as a Government operated initiative to reclaim and grow crops on land in East Africa. Large quantities of machinery were shipped out by the Overseas Food Corporation. For land reclamation this even included a number of second-hand, reconditioned steam ploughing engines. Results were very disappointing and the project was effectively abandoned by 1950.

Meanwhile, the United Nations Food and Agriculture Organization (FAO) was launched in 1948 to encourage food production worldwide. Tractors would be required for future projects.

Undaunted by the failure of their Mectaur, Oppermans produced a replacement for the horse and cart. Their Motocart was a cart with a single front driven wheel providing traction and steering. It enjoyed limited sales while tractors were scarce, although these were not helped by a reputation for tipping over. The recommended service fix was to half-fill the toolbox with concrete!

More successful was Morris Motors' effort at a tractor design. The Nuffield Universal, intended to replace imported American tractors like the Farmall M, John Deere, Oliver and Minneapolis Moline, was conceived as a general purpose tractor with a row crop ability. The engine and gearbox components had been well proved on Morris Commercial military products. The result was a very useful addition to the choice of tractors available.

By 1952 allocation controls were being relaxed and farmers were able to choose from available tractors. It was a time when trends began to become much clearer. Official encouragement was still to 'Plough More, Feed

Left: **Under the stylish fairing lurked renovated 45-year-old Ferguson 20 components and a new Lister engine. The Sutcliffe was aimed at users needing a basic light tractor around a farmstead or for grass mowing. Lack of capital hit the initial launch but it does highlight that old Fergies seem to go on for ever.** *Author's Collection*

73

More'. Tractor dealers started looking for salesmen rather than order takers.

For many farmers the choice lay between Ferguson and Fordson. 'Little Grey Fergies', as they tended to be known, had been pouring off the assembly line in Coventry since 1947, so they were a familiar sight.

The newly introduced 'New' Fordson Major was far superior to the older Fordsons which had given good service. More importantly, it was much bigger than a Ferguson. With a robust drawbar they offered the promise of pulling existing implements. The hydraulic linkage was optional but enabled mounted implements to be attached. These could be bigger than Ferguson implements for higher output. Less sophisticated hydraulics meant most implements needed a depth wheel to regulate penetration. Fordson salesmen knew that other makers were targeting 'its' customers.

Assuming a farmer did not choose from the big two, what were his alternatives?

David Brown had been producing what had developed into the Cropmaster and Super Cropmaster models since 1939. They had earned a good reputation from users who had been allocated one when tractors were scarce.

Morris Motors' Nuffield Universals had a few vices. The vague steering and a tendency to rear up if the front weight was not fitted were two. It had proved a

strong workhorse. With the option of three-point linkage, it made a serious alternative to a Fordson Major. It was relatively easily converted to a three-wheeled layout for row crop work and came with an adjustable sliding rear axle as standard — which was a mixed blessing. With a five-speed gearbox, top gear on the road seemed much faster than any previous tractor.

International offered the Farmall BM, now built in Britain. Based on the M, it had been a very good tractor 10 years before and could still give good service. Only a vaporising oil engine was offered. International had opted to build in Britain to give it a base to sell tractors into the Sterling currency area.

Left: Trading in a tractor was often only the start of a journey. A dealer will often prefer to sell a trade-in away from his territory. To meet this need a number of regular auctions are held each month. These attract dealers and exporters, for often tractors finish their lives abroad. In August 1983 the Lichfield sale included a pair of Fergie 20s, one of which had a Perkins P3 conversion. Others on offer included two MF 590s, a 168 and a 135, as well as a Ford and a Fiat 640. Auctions are cruel places where you can learn the trade's real opinion of the relative worth of any tractor. Fergusons would always sell. *RLM*

Below left: At first sight this looks like an early four-wheel drive conversion. The oversize front wheels are not in fact driven but fitted to enable the tractor to pass over ditches when spraying insecticide in the tropics. The Fordson Major E27N has been modified with a pressurised radiator and a sunshade. The Perkins P6 engine would give extra power. To cope with the heavy steering, Roadless Traction, which did the conversion, has thoughtfully fitted an over-size steering wheel. *Ian Allan Library*

Above right: While not strictly a tractor, the Opperman Motocart was aimed at replacing a horse and cart. Once in position at a job, the hand clutch on the near side could be worked from the ground to move up the cart while loading or unloading. The three-wheel layout was rather unstable when unladen and most Motocarts have had their toolboxes filled with concrete to counterbalance the engine. *Author's Collection*

Right: The single front wheel provides both traction and steering. The clutch is controlled through the flexible cable and the gear lever is within reach of the driver — except during sharp left turns! *Author's Collection*

The Massey Harris 744D was developed from the 44K. A Perkins P6 diesel engine transformed its perfor-mance, turning it into a powerful, slogging drawbar tractor. The seat was mounted on a long leaf spring with its own shock absorber. This 'velvet ride' certainly was far more comfortable than the competition.

Another slogger, the Field Marshall Series III repre-sented 20 years' development of the economical single cylinder, two-stroke diesel engine. Unfortunately, other makers had also been working on developments, including electric starting and more cylinders for smoother running. While still a sturdy tractor, the Field Marshall was beginning to seem rather an old-fashioned choice. Seating on the Marshall was firm and the driver got a good shaking from engine vibration.

In Wolverhampton the Turner Manufacturing Co had introduced the Yeoman of England, fitted with Turner's own V4 diesel engine. This had a fairly unresponsive governor and an offset seating position. Yet there was nothing seriously wrong with the design that could not have been cured by a little more development work.

Another popular wartime import had been the Allis Chalmers B. With its narrow wasp waist and high clear-ance it was ideal for mid-mounted implements. This led to good sales as the light tractor on the bigger farms in East Anglia. Before the development of sprays, a good row crop tractor could be working nearly continuously in root crops.

The Bean self-propelled toolbar was built as a spe-cialist tool for row crop hoeing, which it performed well. It was of no use for normal tractor work.

The BMB President was another small tractor. Built at Southport in the old Vulcan Lorry factory, it was a victim of the factory's location. Much of the prelimi-nary testing was done on local farms with impressive results. What the test team had failed to spot was that the soil in that area was particularly light and free work-ing. On heavier land the results were not so good.

If a light tractor would be sufficient, other con-tenders were Oak Tree Appliances (OTA) and Monarch, both soon to be acquired by Singer Cars, or the Trusty Steed and the Garner. For most buyers, a sec-ond-hand Ferguson probably represented a better buy.

There was one other contender that could do much

of the work of a tractor and more besides. Postwar the Rover Car Company had a problem. The sort of cars it made were not really suitable for export. Without export sales it could not get sufficient allocations of material to build enough cars to keep the factory busy. Impressed by the abilities of an ex-army jeep on his farm, one of the directors suggested that, as a stopgap, Rover should build something similar.

While not a tractor, the Land Rover could pull a load across fields. When it was too muddy for a trailer, it could carry the load itself. It could carry one passenger in comfort, two if the middle passenger kept clear of the gear lever. If the alternative was a long walk across country, four more could cram in the back. With the worst of the clutter removed it could be used for trips to town, possibly towing a cattle trailer. For haymaking or harvest it could tow a loaded trailer or a hay rake. With the potential of 45+mph on decent roads and cross-country ability, it was the ideal tool for an unpredictable boss.

Publicity photographs featured ploughing, cultivation and the use of the optional PTO and belt pulley but that was not where it was at its most useful. Even so, a Land Rover combined the roles of private car and light tractor on many farms. No doubt a few tractor orders were cancelled or postponed if the farmer concerned could obtain delivery of a new Land Rover.

Even after deciding on the make, there was sometimes the choice of diesel or spark-ignition engine. While diesel offered better fuel economy, more cautious buyers would stick with the more familiar spark-ignition.

Ford, Ferguson, David Brown and Fiat could offer the choice. Massey Harris and Nuffield were buying in Perkins diesels, while International was still waiting for a diesel alternative. Turner, Marshall, Caterpillar and Hanomag offered only diesel power.

The smaller tractors were still either straight petrol or fitted with an optional vaporiser.

The reputation of tractors in the field and the local dealer were important considerations in choosing a tractor. Price was a factor but most buyers were shrewd enough to realise that a cheap buy was not necessarily a bargain. Mass production meant a Ferguson TED 20 was £405, or taking the diesel option put the cost up to £525. This made the David Brown equivalent offering of the Cropmaster at £507 for VO and £674 for diesel look dear. Yet a David Brown dealer could rightly point out that its diesel engine had been in production since 1947, while Ferguson and Ford engines were still new and unproved.

Fordson of course had always had a policy of low first cost, so a New Major could be bought for £441 for vaporising oil or £536 for the new diesel. Specifying the

hydraulic lift which was still optional added another £60 to the true comparison. Today we think of the Fordson Major as a powerful tractor but the first models were cautiously rated at only 36hp.

In the same way Nuffields were priced at £465 for the VO model and £570 when supplied with the Perkins P4 engine. Another £80 was needed to get hydraulic lift and PTO. Again Nuffield dealers could claim they were selling a well-proven tractor against the new, unproven, Fordson New Major.

International was looking dear with the BM. The high clearance of this design meant a steady demand for use as a row crop tractor despite the £618 price tag. Even this did not include a self starter, PTO or hydraulic lift.

The Turner was left looking uncomfortably expensive at £717 plus £86 for hydraulics and PTO. It might be worth considering if compared with the rather more powerful Field Marshall, normally sold as a plain draw-bar tractor at £870. Of course, if you wanted a big-wheeled tractor, you could consider the new six-cylindered David Brown 50D at £967.

With tractors more freely available, the logic of relative costs was not lost on farmers. Few Turners were sold once the Fordson New Major was available. Most Field Marshalls went to buyers who needed its rugged

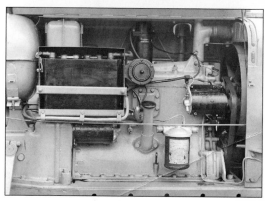

Above left: To save dollars, William Morris, later Lord Nuffield was encouraged to build a large tractor to reduce imports. His targets were probably the International M and the John Deere B. He did not keep it a secret that a tractor was under development and various sneak preview photographs were released. Well-proven components were used where possible. The engine design dated back to 1933 but had recently given good service in military vehicles. The Nuffield Universal was built up from a single massive casting. A special carburettor allowed starting on petrol without the need first to drain paraffin. *Ian Allan Library*

Left: Even with electric starting a magneto was specified, to allow starting by cranking even with a totally flat battery. *Ian Allan Library*

Above: From the beginning the design was convertible between a four- and three-wheel layout. This led to an off-set cranking position for the starting handle and a complex layout for the steering system. *Ian Allan Library*

strength but sales started falling off. Internationals mainly went where specialised row crop work was an important part of the annual workload. Top sellers were Fergusons and Fordsons, with David Browns and Nuffields as the popular alternative choices.

Dollar shortages led to the loss of a number of well-known makes that had given good service. Case, Minneapolis Moline, Oliver and John Deere withdrew altogether. Many International and Allis Chalmers models produced in the United States were no longer available. If a conversion kit from Perkins was available fitting a suitable Perkins diesel engine often extended the working life of existing tractors.

For maximum pulling power a tracklayer was worth considering. Crawlers could keep going in sticky conditions and were still essential on heavy land. With their superior grip, the driver had no worries about wheelspin, so the governor could be opened to the maximum. A crawler driver led a strange, solitary life. His tractor would stay out in the field where he was working. Since he could keep going in wet weather, he needed plenty of sacks and greatcoats to keep out the wet and wind. Cabs were relatively uncommon and the roar of the engine and the clanking of the tracks assaulted his hearing. No wonder a crawler driver sometime seemed very different to his fellow workers.

Caterpillars were allowed in mainly for bigger jobs beyond the capacity of home-market-built tracklayers. This need for tracklayers was met initially by David Brown and County, but later they would be joined by British-built Internationals and Roadless full-tracks. Fowler offered a range including what was effectively a crawler Field Marshall.

The County conversion of the Fordson New Major was a popular option. Although this was built on the New model, the tracks had already been proved on similar conversions of the original Fordson Major (the E27N). David Brown could offer the Trackmaster 30 or 50. Again these were obviously based on the equivalent wheeled models the Cropmaster and the 50D. The Lloyd Dragon was a British tracklayer but used what were basically the tracks from a Bren gun carrier. It looked rather flimsy against the opposition and orders were few. The Bristol was rather smaller and Howard Rotavator offered the Platypus.

If the decision to specify tracks was not clear cut, Roadless offered another alternative. Its half-tracks could be specified on the Fordson Major, Massey Harris, Nuffield or Turner. In theory, if rear wheels were ordered as well, the tractor could be used part of the year as a tracklayer and the rest as a wheeled tractor. Rotapeds were another type of half-track conversion but were fitted mainly to trenchers. Other tracks were

available to slip over rubber tyres. If grip was borderline, strakes or girdles were available to increase grip, especially where the tyres were worn.

Shortages of tracklayers left a commercial opening for importers to try their luck with other makes. Continentals, Hanomags and Fiats were sold in small numbers to buyers who could not wait.

One specialised tracklayer filled a niche: the Ransome's developed 4hp and was intended for use in horticultural applications. The compact hull and the rubber jointed tracks from Roadless produced a tractor that was very controllable and manoeuvrable. Indeed, the makers suggested it could be used inside a commercial greenhouse. Imagine the shower of glass if the driver got too close to the edge. No doubt that thought kept the driver alert!

With more tractors coming onto farms, there was one mystery. Looking at figures compiled by the Ministry of Agriculture, each tractor seemed to replace only two horses. Five factors explain this mystery:

1) Lack of wheelgrip.

2) A limited choice of forward speeds.

3) Implements too small to fully load a tractor.

4) Finishing a job in fewer days.

5) Reluctance of many drivers to operate their tractor at full speed.

Left and right: The gearbox offered five speeds including what seemed a very fast top speed. The rear wheels were adjusted by clamps gripping protruding shafts which hit many gateposts and left their characteristic grooves on many farm buildings. The front axle on the four-wheel model could be adjusted by repositioning bolts. Thoughtful features included a mechanical latch for the built-in hydraulic system. Electric starting, lights, a cushioned seat and a spacious platform made for a comfortable driver.
Both: Ian Allan Library

Below: GOL 108 was one of the prototypes with a different bonnet line and a more elaborate draw-bar. When launched in 1948 the Nuffield Universal was a thoroughly modern and competitive tractor; indeed, much of the initial design was still recognisable 20 years later, on the last of the 10/60s. *Ian Allan Library*

Left: Tricycle conversions of Fordsons were first built in the 1930s to meet the competition from specialised row crop tractors. Although this conversion was engineered for the 'New' Fordson Major, few were sold. The standard row crop axle offered with the Fordson Major had sufficient clearance for most British requirements. *Ian Allan Library*

Below: To prove the stamina of the New Fordson Major, one was set to work for 144 hours of nonstop ploughing in 1955. Just in case, a fully equipped mobile workshop was on standby. To increase traction, optional cast iron wheel weights were bolted to the rear wheel. Have you spotted the three people risking injury during this service stop? With a hard working, hot tractor, taking the pressurised radiator cap off was to risk scalding. By far the most foolish are the two figures under the mounted plough, probably changing the shares. If the chap refuelling was to knock the control lever, either or both could be badly injured as the plough drops on them. *Ian Allan Library*

Right: The trainload of tractors was a popular photographic theme of the early 1950s. It was intended to show readers that Britain's tractor factories were earning valuable export currency, even if home market deliveries were delayed. In this case in 1952, David Brown Cropmasters with later type flat front ends predominate, with a single Trackmaster in the centre. The roping and chocking may look excessive but railway wagons could receive some sharp blows, both when shunting and from normal buffing. *Ian Allan Library*

81

Left: Massey Harris chose the Perkins L4 Diesel as the power unit for its 745 tractor. Almost as soon as it was announced, the Massey Harris takeover of Ferguson threw its future into doubt. Even so, the tractor did sell steadily for several years. Although still related to the old 44 model, part of the cast chassis had been replaced by a steel fabrication to reduce the cost of manufacture. *Ray Bird*

Below left: The Turner Yeoman of England was launched to meet the postwar demand for a sturdy diesel tractor. The cylinder heads of the V4 engine projected from under the bonnet. With a bit more development work, it had the potential to be a good tractor. However, it could not meet the competition of the much lower priced Fordson Major. *Author's Collection*

Above right: What could replace the ex-military jeep which Maurice Wilks had found so useful on his Anglesey farm? As Engineering Director of Rover he had the answer. This was an early prototype of the Land Rover. *Rover Group/Author's Collection*

Below: A Land Rover found many roles on a farm. With four-wheel drive engaged it could pull surprisingly heavy loads, especially over dry ground. It could revert to fetch-and-carry duties when ground conditions deteriorated. In this way it replaced a tractor for many transport and feeding jobs, as well as road-going tasks like moving livestock and fetching spare parts from town. *National Motor Museum, Beaulieu*

Take a typical older tractor on the farm at that time as, say, a wartime Fordson. This could develop at maximum about 23bhp at the engine. The transmission was fairly inefficient, so in practice there would only be about 10-11hp available at the drawbar. This was measured by the pull multiplied by the forward speed. If more than that available pull was needed, the only answer was to change down a gear. Then the available pull was often limited by wheelslip so the engine could not be loaded to capacity.

This was confirmed in tests by researchers, who found that, on average, few tractors were generating more than a usable 8-drawbar horsepower. Another survey only 1 in 7 wheeled tractors being used at maximum engine speed. You can begin to see how horses persisted, especially for the lighter jobs.

They might have appeared old-fashioned but there was still considerable common sense in keeping an old horse or two for odd jobs on many farms. The horse would not be worth much if sold. Many farms still had a worker who was not suited to tractor work. Cold logic would suggest that both horse and worker should be dispensed with in the interests of efficiency. Many farmers reasoned differently. Often they grew crops needing plenty of hand work. Root crops like kale, mangolds and sugar beet needed plenty of hand hoeing to prevent overcrowding of the crop by doubles, or smothering by weeds. Harvesting would probably involve more hand work. Harvesters were being developed in the 1950s, but were still uncommon. Routine jobs like hedging and ditching were still done with hand tools. Until all these jobs had been mechanised there was still a need for skilled hand workers on most farms. Tractor drivers were expected to do their share of hand work. 'Hard work on a farm usually has an ash handle.' This same chap and a horse would be available for carting feed to livestock in the field later in the year and other odd jobs.

Researchers in Australia finally confirmed a long-held belief that good horses could generate much more than one drawbar horsepower. Typically for short periods they found a horse could produce 3hp. It would be cruel to expect this as continuous output but it could be called on to start a wagon moving or when a cart sank

into soft ground. With a tractor the driver would have to select a lower gear instead. The horse's reserve of power is very like that of a steam engine.

One job that was becoming mechanised was threshing. Combine harvesters were starting to become more common. They threshed the grain as it was cut, eliminating the job of threshing in the winter. Something had to be done to deal with the straw left behind, so pick-up balers were introduced. Although combines were affecting the trade of threshing contractors, these were often the people that operated the combine and perhaps a pick-up baler.

Right: **Older tractors tend to get demoted to odd-jobbing. In the early 1950s Nuffield replaced the bought-in Perkins diesel engine with the option of the 3.4-litre BMC diesel from Austin. Early examples, as here, were fitted with radiator slats to allow the engine temperature to be adjusted. You can see how the protruding axle is hidden from the driver's view unless he stands up. The wheel-driven sweeper is being used to tidy up the new permanent showground for the Royal Agricultural Society.** *RASE*

84

There was a certain irony here. Before the combine, long hours used to be spent in the harvest field, stooking sheaves and loading them on to wagons to cart them in for stacking. Pitching the sheaves was hard work, but each forkful was a comfortable lift. Now, with the combine, both the grain and the straw had to be carted, so nearly as much weight had to be carted in, at a time when some of the farm staff and tractors might be occupied combining or baling.

To add to the workload a sack of grain or a bale was an awkward lump to lift unaided. Bales had to be unloaded and stacked. Much of the grain was in four-bushel sacks. These were hired from specialist firms. The railway companies in particular had found this an ideal size for one man to handle with a sack barrow. While 2cwt (or 100kg) was an acceptable weight in docks and warehouses, these had been planned to avoid lifting. On the farm, full sacks needed picking up and unloading, with perhaps extra handling for drying or cleaning at the farm. With the combines, farm staff often found themselves working much harder, trying to avoid the risk of weather damage.

By 1952 the future pattern of postwar tractor production could be seen to be taking shape. Most farms

had at least some tractor power but many still had horses as well. Thanks to the stability of returns from crops and produce, farming was willing to continue to invest in more machinery. Yet there were still plenty of hard, back-breaking hand jobs needing traditional skills and a strong back.

The year 1952 has come to have another significance in tractor history, as it also marks the main watershed between the 'Vintage' and the 'Classic' tractor as defined by the National Vintage Tractor & Engine Club.

Below left: **With the war over, Ford was anxious to replace the obsolete Fordson N. Government controls limited possible improvements and the Fordson Major E27N was a stopgap model. The key improvement was the new design of back axle, which proved to be virtually indestructible. The engine remained largely unaltered. However, from 1948 Perkins offered conversion kits to replace the engine with a P6 diesel, which transformed the pulling power. From 1953 Perkins also offered the four-cylinder L4 power unit conversion, as fitted to this example. When tractors were in short supply, such conversions made a startling improvement. Fuel consumption dropped, especially if the old engine had been getting worn. Pulling power nearly doubled, turning a tired tractor into a useful asset. No wonder this owner felt the luxury of a cab was justified.** *Ray Bird*

Below: Applying extra water to growing crops normally boost yields except in unusually wet years. This redundant Fordson Super Major provides a base to mount a rotary irrigator. Water is pumped to it under considerable pressure, which makes the arms rotate slowly as they spray the ground below. The corrugated shelter keeps the worst of the water off the tractor itself. When the ground is saturated, the tractor is driven to a new position, dragging the supply hose with it. Driving requires the same caution as taxying an airliner! Apart from obstructions, the greatest danger comes from trying to pass under overhead powerlines. *Author's Collection*

6. Relative Stability, 1952-60

The 1950s was the decade when tractors ceased to be simple horse replacements. Implement manufacturers were producing attachments that made best use of the abilities of a modern tractor. What is more, they could make use of far more power than a team of horses could produce, however willing.

Rotary cultivators could absorb all the power a trac-

tor could produce and turn it into tilth. Tipping trailers could make use of all available speed on the road, move useful loads over difficult ground conditions and discharge the load with a movement of the tractor's hydraulic controls. If the tractor had one of the new pick-up hitches, coupling and uncoupling the trailer could be done by the driver from the tractor seat.

The first front-end loaders were starting to replace

Left: **Another thoughtful feature of the Ferguson 35 design was the service flap. By opening this, an operator could both check coolant level and fill up with fuel. There was even a special flange on the tank to direct spilt fuel away from the engine. Even with the bonnet fully tipped, these jobs had been awkward on the Ferguson 20, so this was a welcome improvement.** *Author's Collection*

Below: **It started as a fanciful idea. 'Let's organise a rally only for Fordson tractors'. Commentator Nick Kitchen faces part of the stream of New Fordson Majors parading for Fordson 500. Despite attracting 1,002 entries in all, few tractors were exactly the same. For example, the leading tractor had been modified to row crop specification with a single front wheel. Starting was by an inertia spring starter, so no electrical system was needed. This was a prototype for a potential export order which fell through.** *Author's collection*

Below: As standard the Fordson Major was fitted with fairly light action steering. Yet with front-mounted equipment like a loader it could still become heavy. The power assisted steering kit represented a very welcome reduction in effort. Power came from an under-bonnet hydraulic pump driven off the crankshaft. The hydraulic ram pushed or pulled against the anchorage point. Turning the steering wheel even slightly made the drag link affect a control valve on the top of the ram. Assistance was given until the

valve was once more in the neutral position. In practice, it meant only one hand was needed to steer, leaving the driver free to operate the hydraulic controls or change gear. On the right job it meant a considerable reduction in effort for the driver. A similar Hydrosteer system was soon available for David Browns, Internationals and Nuffields. *Ian Allan Library*

Bottom: While the Nuffield Universal was still selling quite well, it was rather ungainly. Competitors offered compact but still powerful models. Short of funds to produce a new model, the Nuffield Organisation adopted an ingenious method to produce the Nuffield Universal Three in 1958. It was recognisably based on the existing Nuffield chassis. Smaller wheels lowered the clearance slightly but with tight-fitting mudguards the Three looked much more compact. The power unit was based on the 3.4-litre engine but minus one cylinder. The gearbox and the hydraulics were identical. This meant Nuffield had two tractors to offer without major expenditure. *Ian Allan Library*

Below right: The introduction of the Nuffield Three meant the original Nuffield became the Nuffield Universal Four. The rear number plate was mounted on a special bracket so that it could be lifted clear when the ploughing light was in use. *Ian Allan Library*

tedious hand forking. A pick-up baler or trailed combine could be driven by the tractor PTO, rather than needing a separate engine. Cutterbar hedge trimmers could be fitted to reduce winter work. Three-point linkage on other tractors could not embody all the features of the Ferguson system, but it did allow cultivation implements to be made fully mounted, for lower first cost and ease of transport to and from the field.

Few farmers went out and re-equipped suddenly but year by year a new tractor was followed by implements that only it could operate.

Despite grumbles about individual commodity prices, the Price Review system assured farmers that the country wanted and needed all they could produce. This confidence showed itself in a willingness to invest in machinery. This investment often took the form of trading-in even quite modern tractors for the latest model.

There was also a change in climate for both agriculture and the agricultural engineering industry. Rationing and controls were being dismantled. Competition between suppliers was increasing as tractors were no longer being allocated. Prospects for agri-

culture were still set fair, with strong demand for all that could be produced. Different tractor makers responded to these changes in their own ways.

Massey Harris was the leading name in combines, but it led to them ignoring tractor development. To broaden its range it took over the Ferguson company. Although named as president, Harry Ferguson soon fell out with the new owners and retired to pursue his work on four-wheel-drive cars.

Once Massey had control of Ferguson, the business was known at first as Massey Harris Ferguson. First priority was to develop a bigger tractor than the Ferguson 20. This was despite the fact that the Banner Lane Works was still working flat out. Even after nearly 10 years in production and over half a million tractors produced, the Ferguson 20 continued to sell strongly. What emerged was the FE35 in 1956. Resplendent in grey and bronze, it retained the Standard diesel engine but uprated.

The hydraulic system was improved, with two levers. By setting one, the implement would respond to the loads imposed on it by the soil. The other could be used to hold an implement at a given height above ground, or to set the speed of response to the draft control. Most

existing Ferguson implements would fit, but capacity was available to take bigger implements. The de luxe model had a padded driver's seat and a two-position clutch. Press halfway down and the tractor stopped moving, but the PTO and hydraulics continued working.

Two gear levers offered six forward speeds and two reverse. The PTO had two lever positions: in one the PTO was driven from the engine, in the other it rotat-

ed in relation to the tractor's forward speed. Even today, few implements have been built to make use of this feature. The 35's only fault was its reputation for being a bad starter, especially in cold weather. This came from using a Thermostart instead of individual heater plugs in each cylinder. It was not helped by excessive bore wear causing loss of compression.

Two years later the 65 was launched, with a bigger

Perkins diesel engine matched to the 35's transmission. Epicyclic reduction hubs were added at the ends of the back axle, requiring the unusual design of back wheels chosen. Styling was taken from the 40 and 50 models (not seen in Britain). Here was a tractor that could compete with the Fordson Major yet still use existing Ferguson implements.

The next change came with the adoption of a Perkins engine for the 35 in 1959. Choosing the three-cylindered '3 152' produced a classic small tractor. Massey Ferguson having bought Perkins, it made sense to offer its engine. The loss of the engine contract made Standard more willing to sell its works at Banner Lane. These were snapped up by Massey Ferguson, removing the anomaly of buying in its tractors from an independent contractor.

Ford had not been ignoring what was happening at Massey Ferguson. The Fordson Major was being improved by detail changes. It quickly became clear that the diesel engine was by far the most popular choice. This was an excellent starter and proved very economical in use. An effective transmission handbrake replaced a fiddly latch on the brake pedal. The engine power output was gradually increased.

An optional clutch permitted live power take off and hydraulics. This increased the potential work rate for jobs like baling and loader work. Previously, drive to the power shaft and hydraulics stopped when the clutch was depressed. For them to work with the tractor stationary, neutral had to selected in the gearbox and the clutch re-engaged. Most tractor makers soon adopted these features.

Stricter regulations were introduced for the guarding of power take offs. Horrific injuries could follow if clothing got wound onto an unguarded shaft. In time, other regulations would stipulate better guarding for agricultural machinery and tractors. As guards should have been retro-fitted, their absence can be a clue as to when an unrestored tractor ceased being used commercially.

A way of improving wheel grip was introduced and a new expression came into use: 'differential lock'. The differential allows the two rear wheels to be driven at different speeds when turning corners. Unfortunately, it has a side effect. If one wheel can turn more easily than the other, power can be wasted by the differential encouraging that wheel to slip. In sticky conditions a tractor can have only one wheel spinning yet be helplessly stuck.

The 'difflock', as it was soon christened, overrode the effect of the differential by making both wheels turn at the same speed. This reduced wheelspin and increased performance under difficult soil conditions.

The differential was responsible for another vicious trick that has caught out many drivers over the years.

Left: **Implement designers were quick to take advantage of tractors having built-in hydraulic systems. Using this to power external rams brought powerful help around the farm. Few devices were as welcome as the tractor-mounted loader. With a loader attached the tractor was sometimes handicapped for other jobs. David Brown built both the tractor, a 900D, and the loader.** *RLM*

Above left and left: The David Brown 2D was intended as a compact horticultural tractor. Most implements could be mounted directly in front of and below the driver. This gave excellent visibility and precise control. The power unit was a specially designed, two-cylinder diesel and by placing the driver in front of it he had an excellent view of the implements at work. The rear toolbar was ideal for eradicating the wheel marks or for mounting more tines. Both lifts operated by compressed air. While well liked by horticulturalists, David Brown's hopes for the 2D appealing to small farmers were not fulfilled. *Both: Ian Allan Library*

Above: The Deutz tractor was produced by KHD the lorry builders. An effective air-cooled engine was used: it was modular, which made for easy servicing. This was not a model that made it to Britain. *Ian Allan Library*

Imagine descending a slippery slope, say a wet grass field, with a loaded trailer in tow. The driver is relying on engine braking but the engine is speeding up as the trailer is overpowering the braking effect. Quite reasonably, the driver applies the brakes. Much to his amazement the tractor speeds up! What has happened is that with one wheel locked and skidding, the other wheel can run twice as fast for the same engine revs.

Reasoning that applying the brakes is making the situation worse, the driver releases the brakes. Yet the outfit starts to go even faster. What is now happening is that one wheel is rotating backwards with the other running forwards. In this situation the action of the differential means there is no engine braking at all and the driver is sitting on a runaway. If he is lucky, the field will level out and he may regain control. If he is unlucky, a police officer will be telling the sad story to a coroner or fatal accident inquiry.

Applying the difflock prevents one wheel speeding up and improves control. It is not the complete cure because if both wheels lose their grip on a hill, there is a grave risk of the outfit jack-knifing as the trailer pushes the tractor sideways. This can result in the tractor overturning.

An instrument which started to appear on tractors was an engine revolution counter. The first were simple counters which recorded the total revolutions made by the engine. Gearing converted the read-out to correspond to the equivalent of the engine hours run at something less than full speed. This compromise setting met most needs and it did give a way of assessing the amount of use a tractor had had. It was hoped this would lead to more regular servicing.

Similar counters were fitted to some implements. On a grain drill, by counting revolutions of a shaft driving the sowing mechanism, the gearing took account of the drills working to calculate the area sown in acres. On pick-up balers the counter was tripped by the knotter mechanism to count the number of bales made.

As the number of gears increased and power driven implements became common, the driver needed even more information. When spreading fertilizer or spraying

Above: **The Track Marshall was developed from the Fowler VFA but replaced the unconventional Field Marshall engine with a Perkins power unit. Even in sticky conditions with a five-furrow plough, traction was no problem. Both tracks are running on the surface, minimising soil damage. With a crawler, ploughing could continue when conditions had got too bad for wheel tractors. The Suntrac cab gave welcome protection for the driver from the biting winds.** *Ian Allan Library*

Left: **Bigger country estates would sometimes operate their own woodyards. Trees grown on the estate could be felled and converted to usable or saleable timber. This Series IIIA Field Marshall spent its entire working life on one Gloucestershire estate. Fitted with a winch, it hauled felled timber back to the wood yard. Most of its time was spent driving the big rack sawbench as it sawed the trees into planks. The oil from the exhaust mixed with flying sawdust to make a protective coating.** *Author's Collection*

Above right: **Marshalls was conscious that the Field Marshall was losing its competitive edge against more modern designs. Instead of tinkering with minor improvements, it took a radical approach. Powered by a Leyland engine (derated to 70bhp), the MP6 was a big, solid chunk of engineering. It was to be two years before production got under way but it was the talk of the 1955 Smithfield Show. This show was held each winter a few weeks before Christmas. Originally a fatstock show, it developed a reputation as *the* big farming event of the winter. Naturally, machinery manufacturers wanted to exhibit to potential customers.** *Ian Allan Library*

crops, this was a particular problem. Even with the implement correctly set it was possible to increase the application rate by driving too slowly or reduce it by driving too fast. More elaborate counters appeared, based on the design of a speedometer. While they still had an hours counter mechanism, a pointer showed the exact engine revolutions per minute. To make this more useful, scales showed the corresponding forward speed for each gear as well as the correct speed for PTO work and belt work.

Today we would recognise that the driver was getting useful real time information about his tractor's performance. What he did with it was left to him.

Power assisted steering began to be offered as an optional extra. This permitted one-handed steering, speeding up output. Power assist was particularly welcome on tractors fitted with front-end hydraulic loaders. Especially when loaded, they could make manual steering very heavy.

In 1958 the Power Major lifted power output to 50hp at the engine. This left a gap in the market for a smaller

Fordson, which was filled by the Fordson Dexta, powered by a Perkins P3 although badged as a Ford engine. Much of the rest of the design betrayed its Ford Ferguson ancestry.

Nuffield had adopted the diesel engine that Austin brought to the British Motor Corporation. This replaced

Left: Also at the 1955 Smithfield Show was the newly announced International B250, the first International model designed and manufactured in Britain. Designed from the start with a diesel engine, the hydraulic pump was driven off the engine, so here was a tractor with live hydraulics. Disc brakes was another new feature seen for the first time but would later appear on other makes. The B250's compact dimensions gave International dealers a worthy competitor to the Ferguson.
Ian Allan Library

the optional Perkins diesel. Nuffield had left its mark, literally, on many British farms. The original design had featured an American-style sliding axle. This meant that with the rear wheels adjusted to their narrower settings, the shafts stuck out. Hidden from the driver's view, they could do a lot of damage. Many walls still carry scars where a Nuffield was driven too close. One driver produced a spectacular fireworks display by hitting a wooden electricity pole supporting a high voltage line. His hardest job was to feign surprise when he got home to find the power had gone off. The option of a conventional rear axle must have been welcomed by many drivers!

Nuffield's version of the live power take-off was operated by a clutch pedal for the transmission only, and a separate hand lever for the hydraulics and PTO. This enabled the driver to make a tight turn with a trailed implement without damaging the power shaft.

Nuffield joined the lighter tractor trend in a rather unconventional way. To produce a three-cylinder engine they lopped a cylinder off the engine. With smaller rear wheels fitted to the Nuffield chassis, this produced the Nuffield 3. Later, both engines would receive mechanical governors, allowing them to be uprated.

David Browns evolved from the Cropmaster to the 25 and 30, losing their characteristic windshields. In turn they were replaced by other numbered models. The 900, with a short-lived red and blue livery, came in 1956, developing into the 950, 850 and 880. In 1961 came the 770.

It is a curious feature that despite the firm being specialist gear makers, David Browns always had a characteristic transmission sound when running at road speed.

One other model was distinct from this range. At first sight the 2D was merely a self-propelled toolbar. On closer inspection it had a pneumatically operated lifting linkage to raise and lower mid-mounted equipment. The layout, with the engine behind the driver, gave excellent visibility. They had an immediate appeal to market gardeners, who found them ideal for specialist vegetable

growing. Sugar beet growers found them ideal for mounting precision seed drills. The driver could drive and observe that all drills were functioning properly.

Commercially the 2D was not the success David Brown had hoped, believing that it had a place on a general farm. Once again it often made better sense to buy a bigger tractor second-hand for the same outlay, or not to trade in the oldest tractor. On the right job the 2D had the ideal layout. The problem was, not enough customers had the right jobs.

International developed a diesel engine for the M, producing the BMD (British M Diesel). Now it had a competitive big diesel tractor but its dealers had no small tractor to sell. This problem was tackled by the all-British

design B250. Production of this tractor was in the former Jowett works at Idle near Bradford. Fearing comments about tractors built by Idle workers, International always insisted the works were situated in Bradford.

Gone was International diesel design that started as a spark ignition engine and changed to compression ignition when running. Instead these relied on pre-heaters and electric starting in the conventional way. It was a very effective design and laid the foundation for a series of small British-built Internationals.

Sales of new diesel Ferguson 20s were hitting the makers of smaller tractors. A Ferguson user might trade in his three- or four-year-old TEA Petrol Ferguson. When offered for resale by the dealer, it would be considerably cheaper than a new petrol-engined BMB President, a Trusty Steed, an OTA, a Monarch or even an Opperman Motocart. With more power and performance, the used Ferguson usually won the contest for the buyer's order. Later, good used diesel Ferguson trade-ins hit 2D sales.

Singer Motors bought the OTA and Monarch tractors. When, in turn, Singer was bought by Rootes, production stopped abruptly. Brockhouse recognised that major investment was needed to update the BMB President. As a big group, their accountants could see a more profitable return using the money elsewhere, so the President went out of production. They continued offering specialist transmissions. The Trusty Steed and Garner lingered on, produced in small numbers for specialist customers. One potential job was to replace horses towing barges. A major disadvantage was that if the barge hit an obstruction or ran aground, the tension on the tow-rope tended to pull both tractor and driver into the canal!

In the same way, once New Fordson Majors and diesel Nuffields were available, Field Marshalls and Turners looked expensive in comparison. Their simplicity, rugged strength, and the option of a powerful winch helped Marshall to secure some orders, but Turners soon became uncompetitive. Potentially it was a good tractor and with a bit more development time it might have made a mark. Realising the situation, the company concentrated on manufacturing truck gearboxes instead. Marshall's response took longer but was more startling. The Marshall MP6 featured a Leyland six-cylinder engine and a massive chassis. Like its first colonial model, it was designed as an export tractor to meet American competition head on. It overcame most of the objections to the Field Marshall, except that it was too expensive. Most of the tractors went overseas, where they stood up well to intensive work. Marshall produced too good a tractor for its profits.

As more modern tractors were being traded in, export markets started to open up for used tractors. Often they followed the same route as new tractors. By the end of the 1950s Britain was a large-scale exporter of tractors to many countries. This benefited farmers as dealers were willing to take trade-ins against new tractors. Many of the used tractors passed through big, monthly auction sales. Cambridge, Reading, Lichfield and Carlisle sales acted like a stock exchange, setting second-hand values and allowing buyers to obtain what their customers were looking for. With a strong overseas demand taking many tractors abroad, it also explains why examples in preservation are not as common as you might think.

Reviewing this period, the first symptoms of future problems can be seen. Marketing men started to domi-

nate tractor sales. Rather than seeing opportunities to be taken, they began to get arrogant. From their marketing offices they would start to predict how many tractors *should* be sold in a given area. This would then be communicated to the dealer as a target that had to be reached. Should the dealer not reach the target, sanctions would follow.

Henry Ford had pioneered this trend as far back as 1924 when sales were slow and factories were closed, and he was faced with a big payment falling due. To raise money quickly he shipped cars and tractors out to dealers whether they had ordered them or not. As they had to pay on delivery to keep the agency, they borrowed money to pay for the unwanted goods.

This lesson was not forgotten by Ford or its competitors and gradually the relationship between dealer and manufacturer deteriorated. This tended to reverse the former basis, in which the dealer had the initiative. A dealer's salesman would talk to a farmer and assess his future requirements for tractor power. Once he knew what the farmer was trying to achieve, the dealer could

select the most appropriate make and model from among the franchises held.

Effectively, in the early 1950s a farmer could still say, 'I am relying on you to come up with a tractor that suits my needs.' In this way the same dealer might recommend a David Brown 25D as a useful compact tractor, a second-hand Field Marshall for heavy work and perhaps a Fordson New Major for longer distances on the road. For harvesting, a Massey Harris 780 combine. Four makes, one dealer, one happy customer. One nearby local dealer and his mechanics could service most of his needs.

By 1960 the first signs could be seen that dealers were finding their choices more restricted. In turn, customers realised that their trusted agricultural engineer could no longer offer impartial advice. What the marketing men had overlooked was that their ultimate customers were not the dealers but the individual farmers whom dealers had persuaded to consider buying a tractor.

Still, with virtually no tractors being imported and a healthy export trade, what was there for a marketing man to worry about?

Left: Massey Ferguson brought flair to displaying their tractors. Spectators could get an unusual view of this Ferguson 35 as it rotated on its pole. Judging by the gentlemen's attire, it was one of the warmer Royal Shows! *RASE*

Above: Another important way of promoting machinery was to get it to be used at agricultural colleges. Often this would include a photocall when the keys were handed over. In this case the Royal Agricultural College is getting a David Brown 990, with a David Brown Loader, a four-furrow plough and (partly out of the picture) a Hurricane Forage Harvester. Most David Brown Implements were built by their Harrison, McGregor & Guest subsidiary. The reputation of colleges meant that the equipment was often supplied on very favourable terms. It was hoped agricultural students would soon be in positions where substantial machinery orders would be placed. *Royal Agricultural College*

Above right: The showground bus service was another effective marketing idea. Footsore show visitors could get a lift to their destination, while the sponsor's advertising could be read by all. When they were introduced in 1957, local farmers supplied tractors and drivers (in this case a Ferguson with a spacious cab). Makers were soon clamouring to get their latest introduction on the front for exposure. In later years this was often a buyer's first sight of a new model. *RASE*

Right: Proving you can be too far in advance with research, is this Allis Chalmers Fuel Cell Tractor. Propane and oxygen were combined to generate electrical power. It was first demonstrated in America in 1959. The 1008 fuel cells produced enough current to drive a 20hp motor. While attracting wide interest, little more has since been heard of fuel cells. Diesel power continues to become more fuel efficient, meaning that alternative approaches have to beat a moving target. *Ian Allan Library*

7. Heading for Safety Cabs, 1960-70

By the start of the 1960s tractors were the universal power source on all but a very few farms. There was fairly strong agreement between the major manufacturers about the specification to offer their customers.

Diesel power was universal with the option of spark ignition confined to a few specialist export markets. Hydraulic linkage and power take off were standard specification, usually live. The foot-brakes could be used to brake both rear wheels or separated to brake either wheel for tighter turning. Electric starting meant that a lighting system was included. Electricity on the farm meant the belt pulley was very much an optional extra.

With such similar designs these tractors also shared a number of hazards. Any form of driver's weather protection came from an outside accessory manufacturer. With more gears tractors were getting faster, which sometimes led to drivers getting into trouble. Typically

Above: **An occupational hazard of Royalty is having explained to you items of little interest. In this case Her Majesty the Queen is being instructed in the finer points of the Ferguson 35X, as well as the operation of a mid-mounted mower (concealed by a substantial guard). The Duke of Edinburgh, however, was well known to be interested in agricultural machinery. The idea of the mower and Lister tedder outfit was to cut grass while tedding the previously cut row. This promoted quick drying. In favourable conditions, hay could be baled within 48hr of cutting. The 35 was the classic small tractor. Although it went out of production in 1965, similar versions are still produced under licence in India and the former Yugoslavia today. The power unit was a direct descendant of the Perkins P3 engine.** *Royal Agricultural College*

Above: **Ransomes, Sims & Jefferies was** *the* **plough maker for many years. Based in Ipswich, it had to increase its range as tractors got bigger. This was the TS89 reversible four-furrow plough. To lift that clear of the ground needed a big tractor with good hydraulics. To show its potential, it was pulled by a County Super Six which would have coped without trouble.** *RLM*

Below: **The Ford 1000 series shared a common look. Launching four completely new models, and from the new factory at Basildon, entailed a lot of organisation. Many of the transmission components came in from other plants. Ford management made sure it was achieved in 1964, as part of the plan for a World series of tractors.** *Ian Allan Library*

Left: Rail freight was still being used for transporting some new tractors in 1965. Being loaded at Brentwood for Montreal via Avonmouth Docks are a Ford 2000 on the crane and a Ford 3000 already roped down. Each Lowfit wagon could carry a single tractor. To link to the previous models, the 2000 is badged as a Dexta, while the 3000 would be a Super Dexta. *Ian Allan Library*

Below left: With no rail connection to the new Ford factory at Basildon, Silcock & Collings bodied some Albion Reivers as specialist tractor transporters. Each tractor was loaded by Rapier crane at Brentwood goods yard before being roped down. This trainload was made up of the recently introduced Ford 3000s and 5000s. British Railways offered this picture to demonstrate efficient freight handling. It makes a disappointing contrast to Ford's methods of 25 years previously at Dagenham. *Ian Allan Library*

Above right: When first announced, the Massey Ferguson 135 was available without a cab. This allowed owners to specify their own preference. The trailer was a Power X from Adams of Mintlaw, Aberdeen. By lowering the suspension the entire body could be left on the ground like a skip. The late Sandy Adams was a great extrovert and his stand often echoed to loud laughter. *RLM*

Right: This Massey Ferguson 165 had the optional Multi-Power which allowed the driver to make one alternative change of gear on the move. The high lift trailer is seen discharging its load of fresh peas into the lorry waiting to rush them to the freezer plant. As with Ford, there was a strong family resemblance between models. *RLM*

the same brakes were used separately to assist turning the tractor more tightly and together to provide braking on the road. If one brake was more worn, the tractor would slew if braked hard at high speeds.

They were also prone to tip over. This could arise from cornering at speed, working on steep hillsides, falling into ditches or off silage heaps. One particularly nasty hazard arose from a tractor rearing up when stuck or trying to tow an immovable object, especially when using a chain. Often the outcome was that the driver ran the risk of injury, especially if trapped under the overturned tractor. The NIAE (The National Institute of Agricultural Engineering), by now established at Silsoe in Bedfordshire, conducted fundamental research on how this problem could be countered. They

were spurred on by the death toll averaging 35 people per year. There was widespread agreement that something ought to be done but nothing was for a few years.

As far as power went, the commercial failure of the Marshall MP6 convinced most designers that 50hp was as much power as farmers could cope with and 35hp was as small as was required.

Since the major manufacturers were not willing to offer a variety, an opportunity existed for smaller specialist companies. They started by modifying production tractors. County and Roadless had both been building crawler versions of Fordson tractors, Roadless since before the war and County from the late 1940s.

County had already produced its County Fourdrive, which was little more than a crawler with wheels.

Initially it was produced for tropical growers who wanted to be able to cross ditches when hauling sugar cane back to the mill. The two equal size wheels on each side were linked by a chain drive. Steering was crawler style, which was very crude and caused some power loss while turning tightly. Effectively this was the first 'skidsteer' tractor.

Later County four-wheel drive models were engineered with equal sized wheels, with each front wheel shaft driven from the rear wheel.

Roadless favoured imported kits from Italy. These featured conventional front axles as used on military lorries, driven by a propeller shaft linked to a gearbox sandwiched into the transmission. These were often fitted by dealers to both new and used tractors.

In both cases much greater traction could be obtained, especially under difficult ground conditions. Some customers had previously used crawlers but valued the four-wheel-drive mobility on the highway.

Roadless in particular had long cast doubt on the need for four-wheel drive. Its argument was that the front wheels of a tractor with a mounted implement did not carry much weight, so there was little point in driving them. Once they had measured the increase produced by four-wheel drive, they realised that when the rear wheels were slipping, the forces acting to take weight off the front stopped working, and the front wheels were carrying more weight just when the tractor was struggling to push them along. Even so, they only favoured small driven front wheels, with the main work being done by the rear wheels.

Using a 'skid unit' offered an independent maker important advantages. The main mechanical parts of the machine arrived as one ready-assembled unit minus wheels. They were usually shipped bolted down to a big wooden base. Before the general use of forklifts, these used to be dragged around the works like sledges. Hence the name 'skid unit'. Once built up, the machine could be sold with the certainty that the vast majority of mechanical spare parts needed could be bought from a local Ford dealer.

One of the biggest users of Fordson Major skid units had been JCB, which had moved from modifying customers' tractors to producing a purpose-built digging machine.

Once four-wheel drive was established, a demand

By 1961 David Brown had identified a need for more models. The 880 was introduced to fill a gap. By using a bigger engine, a more powerful version of the 850 was produced. The 'Livedrive' badge shows that a double clutch was specified to provide live hydraulics and PTO. The mounted toolbar is being used to form ridges. Even in a publicity photograph issued by the maker you can see how much a driver has to twist to monitor a mounted implement. *Ian Allan Library*

arose for extra power. This was met by fitting a six-cylinder Ford industrial engine which produced machines that were capable of sustained hard work. Four-wheel drive was also a boon on hill farms for extra stability.

Despite the poor sales of the Marshall MP6, some farmers were still looking for more tractor power. Reports appeared in the technical press that Australian farmers were removing the front axle from one Field Marshall and coupling it behind another one. With an implement hooked on behind, and clutch and throttle remote-controlled from the front tractor, this bit of bush engineering made a noisy but effective tractor.

An Essex farmer was doing the same with two Fordson Majors. When his local dealer took an interest, the result was the Doe Dual Drive or Triple D. Both tractors lost their front axles and they were linked by a turntable and hydraulic rams. The tractor was driven from the rear seat. As long as the driver kept his wits about him, this made a very productive tractor.

Independently a Berkshire farmer developed the Paramount Hitch which allowed two tractors not necessarily of the same make to be operated as a single unit.

Some Triple Ds have survived but many were split in later life and exported. Even after Does stopped building them, some users were buying a pair of suitable new tractors to reconstruct leaving the original tractors to be sold.

Other firms started to build tractors. Len Matthews of Horley, Surrey, had built up a useful trade building heavy weight forklifts. His Matbro bent in the middle and effectively consisted of two rear axles driven from one engine and transmission. Bray was building more conventional units with a steerable axle.

With the expiry of the Ferguson patents most competitors took the opportunity to update the hydraulic systems on their tractors.

What we now know were the first signs of a big change came with news that Ford of America was to buy out minority shareholders in Ford of Britain. Once Ford of America was firmly in control, construction of a new tractor factory started at Basildon. Planning was under way for what was to become Ford's 'world' tractors. The same designs would be sold worldwide to all markets. This involved a complete change from Henry Ford's 'build it in one factory' concept.

Components would be transported from specialist manufacturing locations and built up in other specialist plants. Basildon started with the 2000, badged as the

Above: When David Brown offered four-wheel drive, it gave the 1200 more pulling power under difficult conditions. In such sticky conditions a 6-ton load would normally have caused wheel-spin. Driven front wheels made an appreciable improvement and helped get the job done. *RLM*

Right: The British Motor Corporation surprised observers by thinking it had identified a market for a compact tractor. Much of the design work on the BMC Mini Tractor was contracted out to ex-Ferguson engineers. The power unit in 1965 was a diesel version of the A series engine used in the Mini and Morris Minor. Producing only 15bhp, the 950cc engine proved inadequate even with nine forward speeds. (Yet with development, it could have enabled BMC to be a pioneer of small diesel cars.) Initially it was described as a BMC rather than a Nuffield. *Ian Allan Library*

Dexta, the 3000 Super Dexta, the 4000 Major and 5000 Super Major. From the beginning these were badged as Fords rather than Fordsons. Only the model names were carried over. The rest of the tractor designs were totally new.

Buyers were faced with much more choice than before. Four models to choose from rather than two; a choice of transmissions between the conventional six- or eight-speed, two gear lever layout, or the unfamiliar Select-o-Speed semi-automatic gearbox.

Most importantly, it meant that buyers were going to have to think what tasks they wanted the tractor to undertake. Only then could the Ford salesman guide them to the model and specification that was right for their particular requirements.

This had implications for dealers as well. No longer could they order a batch of tractors and assume they would meet the needs of their customers. In most cases they needed a firm order before ordering a tractor of that specification from the factory.

This led to a noticeable change at Fordson dealers. Most of the bigger dealers would have a stock of several tractors on display in the showroom and in the yard outside. They were unsold but available for immediate delivery. These soon disappeared.

Inevitably production was slow getting under way and met a strong demand. As a result, tractors tended to be built against firm orders. Showrooms emptied as tractors were promptly delivered to customers. Any tractors the dealer held tended to be demonstrators, out on farms being tried out against existing tractors.

Once drivers had got used to their differences, the Fords were well received. The new engines were shorter stroked, so they did not have the slogging characteristics of the previous models. Drivers that did not use

plenty of revs complained of a lack of power. In turn, that produced a fussy engine note which made the engine sound over-stressed.

Fords revived an excellent marketing idea. They encouraged fund-raising marathons of tractor work — ploughing, dung-spreading, etc. The drivers were usually Young Farmers of the 'press on regardless' type. While raising funds for a good cause, they demonstrated the amount of work that could be extracted by drivers prepared to thrash a tractor. As well as getting national advertising, they served as an impressive demonstration, both to the drivers taking part and their families who came as spectators.

Right: The Calor Ranger was built by Turner Engineering of Coughton (no connection with Turner Yeoman). A mini engine and transmission drove two Triumph Herald differentials. This gave four-wheel drive in a light but powerful towing unit. With linkage and PTO front and rear it could be used as a low ground pressure machine for jobs like fertiliser spreading. Usually the engine was fitted with a propane conversion. In practice most Rangers were used for turf maintenance or as industrial tractors. *Author's Collection*

Below: Under this familiar shape there hides a Leyland (Nuffield) 10/65 tractor. Like many others, it formed the basis of a JCB digger/loader combination. Modifications included a bigger (engine driven) hydraulic pump and oversize tyres. This, combined with the weight of framework and attachments, gave considerable pushing power. JCB became important customers for Leyland skid units after Ford ceased to supply suitable units. Like many old JCBs, this one is in semi-retirement on a farm, used for odd jobs. *Author*

Select-o-Speed was a transmission with huge potential that failed to catch on. Instead of stopping the tractor to change gear, selecting the gear, and engaging the clutch to move off again, all the driver had to do was move a single lever in a quadrant to select any of 10 forward speeds and two reverse. Here for the first time was the ability to change gear without stopping. Get into a heavy patch of soil and with a click of the lever the driver was in a lower gear without coming to a halt. Lift the implement out of work and a quick movement of the lever, and the tractor was in a higher gear for a quicker turn-around.

Most drivers who used Select-o-Speed praised it. Mysteriously, it did not prove popular in use. Rival salesmen referred to it as the 'lurch-o-matic'. Drivers were encouraged to complain of jerky changes. Second-hand Select-o-Speeds were often converted back to conventional gearboxes to make them easier to sell. In theory Select-o-Speed was as big a step forward as the diesel engine or the live PTO. What went wrong?

Ford was probably a victim of its own advertising. Readers got the impression that it was impossible to make a bad gear change. Driving a Ford, one hand would be on the steering wheel, the other operating the Select-o-Speed control. With no hand to spare to adjust the engine's speed control, most changes were made with the engine running fairly fast. Combine this with perhaps jumping several gears, or from forward to reverse, and no wonder the gearbox was suffering. Who knows? With better driver training and foot speed controls, the Select-o-Speed could have succeeded. Thirty-five years later, changing speed on the move is a feature of most tractor designs.

Could Ford have learned from others' experience? David Brown had introduced and withdrawn an automatic gearbox. There it was felt that farmers were not willing to pay the extra cost. Massey Ferguson offered Multipower. This effectively offered a choice of two speeds, either slowing the tractor for increased pull or accelerating with reduced pull. This carried far less risk of damage, as the ratio jump was only 30%. There was no risk of over-revving the engine as the low speed position did not offer engine braking. While that saved wear on the gearbox, it frightened many drivers who suddenly lost all braking when running downhill!

Tractor manufacturers usually know what their competitors are planning. Massey Ferguson countered the Ford tractors by revamping their range. The 100 series tractors (MF 130, MF 135, MF 165, MF 175) were much more closely related to their predecessors than the New Fords but, even so, it marked the emergence of the unified Massey Ferguson look. Like Ford, a more comfortable seat with better springing was offered. A cigarette lighter was an optional extra.

Originally built as an industrial four-wheel drive, the Bray Centaur had hydraulic linkage front and back. John Suckling, an Essex contractor, used this feature to mount two ploughs and could plough backwards and forwards without turning on the headlands. Powered by a Ford 6-cylinder engine, it was not a commercial success.
The Mike Perkin Archive

Researchers had come to the reasonable conclusion that if a tractor driver was being badly jolted and shaken about, he would tend to slow down. Better operator comfort was sold as increasing output. (Many former tractor drivers, particularly of the late 1950s, will now be suffering back trouble from tractor work.)

As a response to the Ford and Massey Ferguson launches, other makers announced restylings over the following couple of years. David Browns had evolved into the 770, 880 and 990. They carried a chocolate and white livery from 1965. The more powerful 1200 would come later. Allis Chalmers ceased production of the ED40, which was not really a row crop tractor nor a general purpose tractor. It had been powered by the Standard diesel engine and Allis Chalmers recognised that it was not really competitive. No replacement was produced and the

Top: **For robust, good value equipment, Zetor was worth investigating. Originating from Czechoslovakia, prices were usually lower than competing equipment. The forager was also imported. For this demonstration the smaller tractor drives the harvester to highlight the modest power consumption.** *RLM*

Above: **From Hungary in the late 1960s came the Dutra with its characteristic protruding snout. Rugged was a kind description of these machines but they worked well. Most were repowered with Perkins engines but the original Cespel was fitted to this example. The Dutra plant evolved from the Hofherr Scrantz Clayton & Shuttleworth entry in the 1930 Wallingford Trials.** *RLM*

Left: The arrival of the John Deere 4010 in 1962 startled British farming. The commercial failure of the Marshall MP6 had convinced many observers that 70hp was too big for British needs. Yet here was an 84hp tractor from a firm not seen since 1949. The sight of four furrows being turned at 5-6mph made some farmers wonder whether this could be the way forward on their farm. Over 300 were sold in the first three years after the launch, so some willing buyers were clearly found. *Ian Allan Library*

Above: By the mid-1980s the choice on offer had been widened considerably. John Deere gradually accepted the need for smaller tractors and the desirability of four-wheel drive. At first only hydraulic assist was offered but the next series of models had true mechanical drive to the front axle. Top left: the 1140 at 56DIN hp was a relatively small offering from the old Lanz works at Mannheim; bottom left: the 82hp 2140 had the benefit of *mechanical* front-wheel drive for extra traction; top right: the 3040 was rated at 90DIN hp with mechanical four-wheel drive; bottom right: the 4240 was designed as a two-wheel drive machine but hydraulic assist was offered for extra grip. At 128DIN hp it was a big comfortable tractor with the Sound Guard cab with its characteristic curved door. *RLM*

Land Rover exhibited a 5-ton payload prototype at the 1969 National Grassland Demonstration. A hydraulic drive powered the front-mounted, double-chop harvester. The body was based on a Farmhand dung-spreader to enable one man to do the cutting and carting on his own. While the Land Rover prototype was not taken further, another two units on Unimogs were built by the SMO-MOT team. Seeking an alternative product, they went on to become Whale Tankers and established an international reputation. When you consider the innovations they have introduced in that market, their change of direction was agricultural engineering's loss. *Mark Fisher*

firm concentrated on construction machinery and implements. In the US, Allis Chalmers was demonstrating a prototype fuel cell tractor. Even 35 years later it is still in advance of anything yet in production.

At first badged as a BMC, Morris Motors caused general surprise by introducing its Mini tractor. Similar to the grey Ferguson in appearance, it was powered by a 950cc diesel engine based on the Morris Minor petrol engine. The power output of 15hp was thought to be sufficient for many around-the-farm jobs.

Much of the design was by former Ferguson engineers on contract. In practice, most Minis seemed to finish up pulling gang mowers.

Nuffield had offered the 10/42 and 10/60 as 10-speed versions of their tractors for some years. These were now restyled with the fuel tank mounted in front of the radiator and a slight boost in power.

The introduction of the new Fords helped Nuffield in a curious way. Ford was unwilling to continue to supply JCB after the model change. Joe Bamford made a highly publicised flight to Detroit to persuade Henry Ford to change his mind. Having failed in his mission, the next

JCB models were built on Nuffield skid units. Booming sales of JCBs increased Nuffield sales considerably.

International had extended its range; the B275 and B414 were descended from the B250. The B450 followed on from the Super BMD while the B614, 706 and 806 were added.

Another new small tractor was the Winget, powered by a single-cylinder Lister diesel engine, launched by Slater & England of Gloucester. In contrast, County and Roadless were joined by Northrop, later to be succeeded by Muir Hill, in producing four-wheel-drive versions of the new Ford tractors. All three makers were producing six-cylinder versions for extra power. Doe was building Triple Ds with two Ford 5000s as the 130. Matbro was building the Mastiff. Tony Flower of Devon introduced an 85hp Power Pack power unit with hydraulics and PTO but no transmission. Using a six-cylinder Perkins engine, It could be used in place of a static tractor to drive a pump or other PTO equipment.

At this point the major British tractor makers were clearly not offering what some customers really wanted. Four-wheel drive had to be obtained by using a specialist converter and resulted in a higher cost per horsepower. Again, if high horsepower was required, it was available only from the converters and modifiers.

Other tractor makers were willing to fill the gap. Zetor of Czechoslovakia, through Skoda Great Britain, offered a range of Zetors: the 2011, 3011, 3045 and 4011. To British eyes these were crude but rugged tractors — cheap too. They proved very popular on hilly farms where four-wheel drive was valued more for extra control on sloping ground.

One unexpected result of the arrival of Zetor was a

Above: **A driverless tractor sounds straight from science fiction but Peter Finn-Kelcey came up with a near approach. A wire was buried along the route the tractor was to follow. A guidance system detected the position of the wire and corrected the steering as necessary. If the tractor 'lost its way', it stopped immediately. The safety rope at the front stopped the engine if it struck an obstacle or animal. When this was developed in the mid-1960s, electronics was a young science. Now wire guidance is relatively well known for industrial trucks but then it was most disconcerting to observe. It enjoyed a limited success, especially in orchards.** *RLM*

Right: **Diagram of the installation of a Roadless conversion to a Ford 5000. The gearbox is sandwiched into the existing transmission with a drive shaft to the front axle. Drive to the front axle can be engaged when required. Until the arrival of safety cabs, it was relatively easy to transfer the kits between tractors. Typically a farm might fit the kit onto two or three tractors in turn.** *Author's Collection*

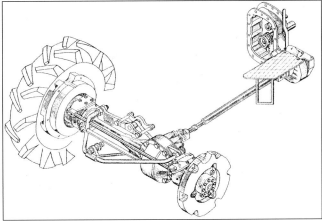

boost to smaller agricultural engineering companies. Typically a farmer's son or skilled engineer fancied having a go on his own. With a good local reputation before starting business, the first servicing and repair jobs would come his way and perhaps the offer of some premises to rent to provide a workshop. The next logical stage was to deal in second-hand machinery as well as fast-moving spare parts.

At this point they would encounter the arrogance mentioned earlier. The local main dealers would give only a nominal discount on spares. As for getting a worthwhile tractor agency — no chance. Yet sometimes the existing local agent was complacent and offered poor service.

These enterprising chaps flocked to Zetor and other imported makes. Even if an existing main dealer had felt that his customers would like a cheap four-wheel drive tractor, the arrogant marketing men insisted on a single make policy. No sensible business would give up a good franchise for an unknown quantity. As a result, Zetor, Ursus, Belarus and Dutra tractors were mainly sold by keen, ambitious, young businesses anxious to establish themselves.

The established dealers referred contemptuously to 'Iron Curtain tractors', 'subsidised dumping' and 'poor back-up'. They found themselves up against enterprising new dealers who really wanted business from their customers. Typical buyers were farmers who had resigned themselves to buying second-hand. Gradually over the years these unfamiliar names of tractors spread. Many of today's well-established dealers date back to a start promoting unfamiliar tractors to doubting farmers.

Dutra offered a rugged four-wheel-drive tractor with the option of a Perkins diesel. The Dutra works evolved from the prewar HSCS factory. Few were imported, but they were well thought of. Holder and Eicher could offer compact four-wheel drive tractors designed for vineyard work.

The most significant import was the return of an old familiar name: John Deere. Deere had abandoned the two-cylinder layout that had served it so well, going straight to a six-cylinder engine and remarkable power ratings. The 4020 offered 91hp in two-wheel drive layout, while the 5020 offered 131hp also on two-wheel drive.

Bear in mind this was nearly twice the horsepower of the biggest British-built products at the time, apart from the converters. At first most people shook their heads but far-sighted farmers placed their orders. They realised that new implements would be needed but they were attracted by the amount of work these giants would get through. To help with their decision making, John Deere paid for the cost of a consultant's report on the financial implications to the potential customer of buying such a big tractor.

Deere arrived with an excellent reputation, so it could be rather more discriminating in selecting dealers. In common with the other importers it could survive on quite a low sales penetration. Much of the initial sales promotion went into building on its reputation. This was probably not charged into the price of each tractor sold so that the company could afford to sell only a small number of a tractor being produced in quantity for some other market.

Over the next few years other overseas and European makers would be attracted to try their luck in the British market.

Once JCB had established that there was a demand for self-propelled digger loaders, other manufacturers started to supply similar units based on agricultural tractors.

In 1967 Ford introduced its first European-built machines, based on the 4500 Industrial tractor. The excavator and loader assemblies were manufactured in Denmark using a British-built Ford industrial tractor and cab.

Above: **When mainstream manufacturers failed to meet a demand for increased tractor power for large scale cultivation, Versatile of Manitoba, Canada, stepped in. This was primarily an assembly operation, using Cummins diesel engines, and well-proven earthmover components. By using the pivot steer principle, the need for a steering axle was eliminated, yet all four wheels could be driven. From this early example grew a range of specialist tractors for North American conditions, including the 555 alongside.** *Author's Collection*

Left: **Muir Hills were built at Gloucester in the Railway Carriage Works. When introduced, they were among the most powerful tractors available. With 15 years' hard work under its belt, this early 101 was still working well with a spring tine cultivator. The transmission layout meant that the driver was seated high in the air. They were superb tractors to drive, with power steering and a wonderful feeling of being on top of the job. Effectively, this was a new tractor in its own right, rather than a conversion. Yet by using many Ford parts, spares were easily obtained.** *Ray Bird*

Wain Roy was building similar machines on David Brown 990 skid units. Massey Ferguson was still offering machines based on the 65 and 35 agricultural tractors. Steelfab of Cardiff was building on International B275 units.

Fiat crawlers were imported by Manns of Saxham, the Claas dealers, while Leefords brought in a tool carrier from East Germany.

Farmers were beginning to discover that there were alternatives to a British-made tractor.

8. THE SAFETY CONSCIOUS ERA – 1970 ONWARDS

As mentioned, concern had been growing about the number of drivers injured and killed by crushing by overturning tractors. Safety frames or cabs were suggested, to offer better protection. Bonser of Nottingham had offered a safety cab for some years, based on research work done by the NIAE. While it offered protection from over-turning, it was cramped and noisy for the driver.

It was clear that major design work would be needed to offer a protective frame without interfering with attaching implements to tractors. Not only did it have to be strong, but the tractor it was attached to had to withstand any strain imposed on the mountings without breaking.

It was decreed that all new tractors driven by workers should be fitted with an approved frame or cab from mid-1970. Approval would be granted to a cab or frame only after an impact test carried out by swinging a massive weight on the end of a chain. Apart from damaging the frame being tested, the test itself was expensive and the cab had to be tested on the make and model of tractor for which approval was sought. While the cost of this proce-

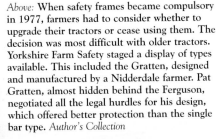

Above: When safety frames became compulsory in 1977, farmers had to consider whether to upgrade their tractors or cease using them. The decision was most difficult with older tractors. Yorkshire Farm Safety staged a display of types available. This included the Gratten, designed and manufactured by a Nidderdale farmer. Pat Gratten, almost hidden behind the Ferguson, negotiated all the legal hurdles for his design, which offered better protection than the single bar type. *Author's Collection*

Left: A popular theme for press photographers is the ceremony of 'handing over the keys'. Wiltshire farmer Mr William Collet recalls it was his first Quiet Cab. He felt deafened by his previous tractor cab and when he was persuaded to try the Fiat in 1975 on the same implement, the reduction in noise convinced him and he bought it on the spot. It proved a good tractor during the three years he kept it. Such positive feedback from the first British customer should have worried marketing people at British tractor makers. Driver comfort was to become an important sales feature in the future. *Wiltshire Times/RLM*

dure was negligible for a volume producer, it badly affected the economics of producing a tractor in small numbers.

In the usual British way there was big backlog of cabs waiting to be tested by the NIAE, which had the only test rig able to issue the appropriate certification. Ironically, Bonser, the original pioneer of safety cabs, found that its design — which had been proved in practice — would not pass the test.

While the safety cab legislation saved some lives, it changed the appearance of tractors in regular use. The intention of the legislation was that safety cabs or frames should be fitted by the dealer as specified by the customer. In practice, tractor makers planned ahead to supply tractors already fitted with cabs to dealers. While boosting their turnover, it also meant that buyers could not buy a tractor without a cab even when they were permitted to do so. No doubt the families of the those killed by overturning tractors would agree that was entirely right. The high noise levels in early safety cabs resulted in legal noise limits being set, producing the so-called 'Quiet Cabs'.

The problems started when it was enacted that existing tractors in use should also be fitted with safety cabs or frames. Many of the perfectly serviceable tractors on farms had been made by makers who were no longer interested in keeping them in service: Marshalls, Olivers, Minneapolises, Allis Chalmers and Turners, for example. Other models came from manufacturers who regarded them as obsolete. They made no effort to ensure a safety frame would be available at a sensible price to fit; for example, the Fordson N, Massey Harris

or Fordson Major E27N. If these were to be fitted with safety frames, somebody would have to do something. Quite rightly, most potential cab makers had concentrated on models with large numbers still on farms. For rarer models nobody considered it worth offering a safety cab, so effectively they could only continue to be used unprotected by the actual owner. It was around this time that a number of interesting old tractors were left in the shed permanently.

A few enterprising individuals developed alternative frames and had tests done at the Dutch testing station, which relieved the backlog. Naturally, they too sought approval for the more popular makes like Ferguson 20s and Massey Ferguson 35s.

The practical effect was that no suitable frame was available for such popular tractors as Fordson Ns, Field Marshalls, most prewar makes and Allis Chalmers B types. Suddenly it was no longer possible to keep the reserve/spare tractor(s) on the farm legal. Quite a number of people were surprised to find they had acquired a new hobby almost by chance. Often the first stage was simply to decide not to scrap that interesting old tractor that could no longer legally be used. While many were scrapped, others were parked up in sheds unused. These spare tractors probably did relatively few hours each year but would be used to pull out seed for drilling, hay turning, bale carting — all the small jobs it was not worth using a newer tractor for. This was often the tractor driven by the schoolboy or the part time helper.

The effects of safety legislation reduced the population of spark ignition engines. With falling demand, the oil

Left: **Mention Lambourn cabs to most tractor drivers and they will think of simple canvas-covered shelters. This sleek and stylish Quiet Cab was offered by Lambourn. It blended well with the styling of the Massey Ferguson 275. Legally, a farmer could specify his choice of cab to be fitted by his dealer. In practice, most makers insisted on supplying dealers with tractors complete with cabs, effectively reducing the choice available. Lambourn's only potential customers were farmers converting tractors bought before 1970. Few farmers were willing to spend more than the cost of the cheapest frame.** *RLM*

Above: **Fitting a heavy duty loader tended to render a tractor less handy for other jobs. Some farmers opted to buy a specialised industrial digger/loader instead. This Massey Ferguson digger evolved from an agricultural tractor originally, so it was a fitting choice. The load is a single Howard Big Bale. The driving cab and the grapple both offered the driver protection if the load was to spill over and fall back off the loader.** *Author's Collection*

Right: **If a machine is not commercially available, many farmers will build their own. In this case the mast of an old Coventry Climax forklift has been fixed onto the back of a Ferguson 35. This enables the outfit to pick up a potato box and travel with half a ton of potatoes at a time. Certainly this was not pretty to look at and was rather hard to drive. Its length made it hard to manoeuvre. One factor encouraged the driver to persist. If it was not for this crude device, there would be a lot more physical effort needed to get the load stacked or moved. Once the need for a forklift had been proved on a farm, such an outfit would soon be replaced by something more sophisticated — once something was commercially available.** *Author's Collection*

companies would soon cease to produce fuel for them.

Overall, mainstream manufacturers could be fairly complacent. Over the last 70 years the tractor had gone from a dream for the future to what was a soundly engineered piece of equipment that had enabled farmers to increase yields and hold down the cost of food. Abundant, cheap food meant that few people were going hungry. It also meant that with less money needed for food, it could be spent on the luxuries of modern life.

The tractors they were building were soundly designed and economical with fuel, reasonably comfortable to drive and able to cope with most of the implements farm-ers wanted to use with them. They were reliable enough for a farmer to be very put out if a tractor failed to start. A few imported tractors were coming onto the British market but some of these were from factories owned by the same parent company as the British business. Thanks to the safety cab legislation, they felt sure a major investment would be needed before any newcomer could disturb their comfortable situation.

Three facts ought to have disturbed any mood of self-satisfaction, for their complacency was soon to be shaken. For some unaccountable reason, a few farmers were paying out large sums of money for machines that were doing a tractor's work but were not tractors.

Crawlers with bulldozers and Drott loading shovels had been bought by a few big farms for construction jobs, road repairs and loading muck and silage. Almost imperceptibly at first, more farmers were buying digger-

loader combinations instead of fitting a loader onto a tractor. Bought almost on a whim, once on the farm they tended to work many more hours than expected.

Mounted forklifts were becoming available to handle loads on pallets. These saved labour but were cumbersome and awkward to drive. Then it was possible to buy a forklift on a tractor where the direction of travel had been reversed. Now the driver could face his work. Then other firms offered muck forks and buckets that would fit a self-propelled forklift. With the weight on the drive wheels, these could outperform a tractor and loader. Volvo and JCB had sold one or two of their big industrial shovels as farm loaders.

People scoffed that equipment was far too spe-

Above: When it wanted a big tractor, R. A. Ince built itself *Bruno*. Most of the components were sourced from earthmoving plant. While the Ince did not go into production, it may have encouraged tractor makers to offer larger models on the British market. *RLM*

Below: While gas turbines have not yet been used for agricultural tractors, they did make an impact in tractor pulling. The 'Green Monster' bears as much relation to a tractor as Formula 1 cars to a Land Rover. The sport draws the crowds. Farm boy engineers can experiment with combinations undreamt of by respectable engineers. Incidentally, the rules (yes, there are some) stipulate that the exhaust jet points upwards. This can lead to unexpected hazards indoors, as sponsor's banners hanging from the roof get fried in the jet blast. The driver here is Art Arfons, better known for his attempts on world speed records. *RLM*

Above: **Belarus tractors from Russia were sturdy, no-frills machines. They did offer value for money. This 52hp MTZ52 cost £1,200 in 1971; for a four-wheel drive 72hp tractor, that was very reasonable. Not surprisingly, farmers were keen to investigate this overseas alternative.** *RLM*

cialised. To see them actually tackling their work so efficiently tended to change opinions. Always the final result was the same, whatever the machine. Once bought, it was doing more work than expected.

Farmers and dealers were taking more interest in the offerings of importers. Perhaps they were aware that control of British tractor makers was moving away from Britain. Also, the early safety cabs tended to be noisy and cramped.

These factors would affect the future. Predicting the future is normally a no-win situation. If people believe your predictions, time will prove you wrong for certain. If your predictions are correct, anybody who knows anything about the industry will laugh at them and say they are wrong.

Imagine the scorn that would have been poured on the following predictions if they had been made in the late 1970s. The sobering thought is that as these 'predictions' were written in 1999, they have already happened.

- All except one of the well-known tractor manufacturers will change hands, many of them to the most unexpected owners.
- Declining farm incomes will ensure that many tractors built in the 1970s will still be at work at the end of the century (so it is still too soon to consider them as history).

- Fashion conscious youngsters will pay premium prices to wear clothes carrying a crawler trademark with no idea what it means.
- The best place to buy dog food, horse bandages or a wax jacket will be from the parts department of your local main tractor dealer. One British tractor factory will be redeveloped as a supermarket.
- Tractor manufacturers will make more money out of arranging finance than manufacturing agricultural machinery.
- Farmers in Europe and America will be prevented by their governments from growing food, while in Africa people starve.
- It will take a wheelwright and his son in Lincolnshire to show tractor designers what their customers really want.
- If a tractor driver wants to know where he is, instead of looking round he will rely on signals from space. When plotted, his instrument panel will tell him where he is, where he has been and what he has done.
- By the end of the century a typical tractor buyer will expect to get a tranquil tractor cab even at full power, with radio, stereo, air conditioning, CB radio to chat to other local tractor drivers and home, an in-cab computer, the ability to change gear on the move under load, power assisted brakes with connection for braking an attached trailer, power steering, four-wheel drive and at least 150hp under the bonnet. Many will want a 40mph top speed.
- The farm office will be in the cab of a modern tractor. Mobile phones, lap top computers, and on-board computers will mean many business decisions can be made while driving a tractor. This will be just as well as declining farm incomes will continue to reduce the number of employees available to drive.
- Atomic power, gas turbines, fuel cells, steam power or the Stirling engine may still be the power sources of the future but none will make it into a commercial tractor before the 21st century. However, turbo charging, intercooling and electronic engine management will transform the diesel engine of 1970.
- So many people will get interested in the history of vintage tractors that tractor shows will attract big crowds. Indeed, people will even be reading books on the history of tractors. (Just like you are!)

No doubt even more fascinating developments are in prospect for the future. We will have to wait and see.

POINTERS TO THE FUTURE

The following are 10 tractors which, at the time of launching, farmers were not quite ready for. With hindsight, we can see they have influenced future trends.

Right: **An** alternative to a conventional crawler track was this 'elastomeric track' offered by Track Marshall for a time. With 200hp available from the engine, the problem was to turn it into *useful* pulling power. It was hoped that it would prove less costly in terms of track wear on certain soil types. The other advantage was the ability to travel on the road between jobs. While Track Marshall still builds conventional crawlers it is worth recalling that the first rubber tracks were tried in the late 1930s. *RLM*

Below: **In** 1973 Valmet of Finland introduced its six-wheeled drive tractor. The big rear wheels were replaced by two smaller wheels rocking around a common pivot. Although it created a lot of interest most of the limited sales were to peat processors which often fitted tracks over the rear wheels for extra grip. The curious-shaped cab roof predated air conditioning and was supposed to give the driver shade. *RLM*

Left: Proving you do not need a big factory to produce a big tractor was the FTD. This eminently practical machine used a Ford 5000 transmission, new six-cylinder Ford engine, Schindler front axle and a Duncan cab. The result was a cost-effective high-horsepower tractor. Effectively, these were built to order. Farm Tractor Drives was run by Arthur Battelle, the noted novelist and Ford tractor historian. FTD was taken over by a main Ford dealer and soon shut down. *RLM*

Below left: Even without a cab the White Field Boss was spectacular. When the chrome brightwork was polished it fairly sparkled but ignoring the bright trim there was a substantial tractor underneath, specified for many long hours in the field. The author once had a stand at the Royal Show opposite a Field Boss. Tractor drivers were positively drooling at the idea of driving one! *RLM*

Above right: The Trantor design team took a fresh look at tractor design. Sprung suspension, high road speed and powerful brakes distinguished its offering. The tractors were innovative and ambitious and could be said to have laid the foundation for modern high-speed tractors. Passengers could be carried and there was a load space in the back. Where considerable road work was needed Trantors acquitted themselves well. A typical job would be hauling a vacuum tanker, as shown here. *RLM*

Below: Despite its futuristic look most of the main components of the County FC1174 were well proved. It had the strength of a normal four-wheel-drive tractor with the room to transport specialised equipment. Converters like County were able to bring to the market machines that bigger companies would not be willing to make. County machines enjoyed a good reputation and many are still in use, albeit rather battered. *RLM*

Above: When demonstrating a tractor the dealer often attaches a board showing his name and address. PM Tractors at Peterborough found its board rather small when fixed to a 'Ford' FW30. With a nine-furrow reversible plough this Steiger-built machine could get through a lot of work. In practice, rather like crawlers, most worked relatively few hours each year. They will have a long life expectancy. One disadvantage is that their size makes it difficult to travel on public roads without an escort. *RLM*

Left: Fendt Tool-carriers lent themselves to be readily converted to what were specialist machines. In this case a rear-mounted sprayer is fed by an additional tank mounted in front of the cab. This can be easily removed using the tipping subframe underneath. After a few minutes' work the equipment could be detached leaving a useful tractor ready for the next task. The Tool-carrier offered a forward vision of a row crop tractor with power of a normal tractor. *RLM*

Above: The Dutch Lely company pioneered the reversible tractor concept. It could power a forage harvester, as shown in the drawing in the background, or tow conventional implements. The power harrow fitted could make effective use of a lot of PTO power. The hydrostatic transmission gave self-propelled flexibility in forward or reverse speeds. While the tractor quickly went out of production it did have a strong influence on other designers. *RLM*

Below: Tyre treads are often a guide to how hard a tractor is working. From the state of the tyres this five-furrow Lemken reversible plough was demanding plenty of power. The driver could relax knowing there was more than sufficient on tap. Under the bonnet was a 240hp MAN diesel and the outfit weighed just 10 tonnes. That made a formidable machine for 1970 when it was introduced. Schlüter started building tractors in 1937 and the 2500 VL was its biggest conventional machine although it could build up to 500hp. Marketing was low key and mainly by recommendation. *RLM*

And finally...New Holland presents its new range. In a spectacular finale, the demonstration team attempts to climb on each other. While the bemused audience wonders what on earth is going to happen next the narrator can ram home the sales points. The power, comfort and refinement that will be enjoyed be drivers well into the 21st century would be far beyond the imagination of any of the early pioneers.
Author's Collection